The REAL BOOK *About*

PREHISTORIC LIFE

The REAL BOOK About

PREHISTORIC LIFE

by Dorothy E. Shuttlesworth

Illustrated by
Matthew Kalmenoff

GARDEN CITY BOOKS, GARDEN CITY, N. Y.

DEDICATED TO THOSE PEOPLE
WHOSE VISION, COURAGE, AND HARD WORK
HAVE MADE POSSIBLE AN UNDERSTANDING
OF OUR EARTH'S EXCITING STORY

My warmest appreciation goes to the following staff members of the American Museum of Natural History.

Dr. Edwin H. Colbert, curator of fossil reptiles and amphibians, for his kindness in reading and criticizing all of the manuscript concerned with paleontology. Also to Junius B. Bird, associate curator of archaeology, for a critical reading of the section concerned with archaeology, and to Dr. James Ford, associate curator of North American archaeology, for an enlightening discussion of the Mound Builders' culture.

Contents

The REAL BOOK *About*

PREHISTORIC LIFE

Chapter 1

BONE DIGGERS DISCOVER THE PAST

Suppose we come upon a letter yellowed with age, which was written by someone during the Revolutionary War. Nearly two hundred years old! Such a direct contact with "the past" stirs the imagination; we try to picture all the activity taking place at the time it was written. Then someone shows us an Indian arrowhead found in a grassy meadow. Suddenly the letter of Revolutionary times seems very recent, as the Indian relic speaks of the days before pen and paper were known on this continent, when the meadow was the homeland of a primitive tribe whose living depended on hunting. So much has been changed in North America within five hundred years, the Indians' world seems almost unbelievable. Still, a great many pieces of evidence have been found to help reconstruct the way of life of the earliest Americans: the pottery they made, their clothing, tools and weapons, and various forms of art work.

But then let us take a really giant step backward, where even five hundred years is an almost unnoticeable speck of time. One way to do so is to gaze upon the fossil skeleton of the giant dinosaur, Tyrannosaurus—a creature which, like the Revolution and the Indians, belongs to the story of our continent but which was on the scene almost a hundred *million* years ago. We need much expert advice if we are to visualize the life and times of this great beast! Scientists tell us Tyrannosaurus lived in a part of the western United States which now is dry and desertlike, but in the dinosaur's day was covered with marshes, grassy plains and forests. They give us a lively picture not only of Tyrannosaurus and his neighbors but of creatures and events of still earlier years. It is a fascinating story; and just as exciting is the account of how man has learned what took place long before human beings existed.

The keys that have unlocked the mysteries of life before recorded history are fossils—fossil bones, fossil plants, fossil shells, fossil molds, even pieces of fossilized skin. But even fossils have their puzzling aspects. We know that a fossil bone is one that comes from a past geologic age, one that probably has been transformed into stone and represents a kind of animal or plant that no longer exists. However, once we understand that such remains of past ages do exist, we may wonder why they are discovered only in certain areas. Why are they not equally common in all parts of our country and on other continents?

The preservation of a fossil requires certain conditions. As a rule flesh and bones eventually decay and disappear, but a combination of circumstances may change this. When some animal of the past died in a location where its body was soon covered by mud or desert sands, the decaying process was slow. The bones and shell, especially, remained intact for a while and, if conditions were just right, as these hard parts began to break down, the original substance was infiltrated or replaced by mineral matter. The result: a fossil. Rarely a soft part, such as skin, decayed slowly, and was affected rather rapidly by mineralization, so that it also was fossilized.

Plants were preserved as fossils in two ways: the woody parts such as stem, trunk and branches were turned to stone by minerals that seeped into their

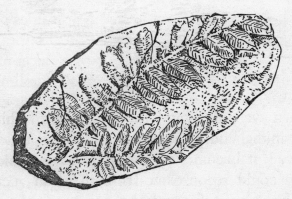

Fossil fern

cells; or the clear imprint of leaves and even flowers were made in rock or coal as these substances hardened. Many important "animal fossils," also, are not actual remains of the creature, but indicate something about it. Footprints, the form of an animal's body which decayed or dissolved after leaving an impression in rock, burrows and nests, all have contributed much valuable data for scientists. They are found as molds, looking as if they were made by a talented prehistoric sculptor.

Footprints

When we understand the hit-or-miss fashion in which animal and plant life of prehistoric times was preserved, it becomes all the more remarkable that anyone could reconstruct from them an accurate, coherent story. Of course no one person has done

16

this. For more than a hundred years scientists have been working with fossils to unravel the secrets of the earth. First by chance, later by determined hunting, they collected innumerable specimens and worked over them to give them meaning. These experts are known as paleontologists.

Strangely enough some of the beginnings of this tremendous work were made by children. An Englishman named William Smith was one of them. Nearly a hundred and fifty years ago he made a boyhood hobby of collecting rocks, to which he was able to add occasional "rock bones" that came to his attention. He chose to be a surveyor so that he had constant opportunity to study the earth, and became aware that its hard foundation was not one solid block of rock but was made up of layers. The "layers," he reasoned, belonged to different ages and each had its own kind of fossils—types that were not found in younger or in older layers. Surveyor Smith began to match rock layers, using fossils as guides, and worked at the project until he had a diagram of the earth's aging over hundreds of millions of years. Fossils could not be "interpreted" without a knowledge of rocks, nor could rocks be understood as they are today without knowledge of fossils.

Over the years a time scale was worked out which divides the whole of geologic time in this way: the biggest divisions are called "eras." Eras are divided into "periods." Periods may be divided into "epochs." In popular use, divisions of time are often known

Time Chart

Eras	Periods	Approximate Years of Duration	Important Types of Animal Life
	Recent		
Cenozoic 70 million years	Pleistocene	1 million	
	Pliocene	10 million	
	Miocene	15 million	
	Oligocene	10 million	
	Eocene	19 million	
	Paleocene	15 million	
Mesozoic 140 million years	Cretaceous	60 million	
	Jurassic	35 million	
	Triassic	45 million	
Paleozoic 350 million years	Permian	25 million	
	Carboniferous	50 million	
	Devonian	65 million	
	Silurian	40 million	
	Ordovician	75 million	
	Cambrian	90 million	
Proterozoic Archaeozoic Azoic	No fossil records from these eras..................		

as "ages," as the Age of Fishes. The eras from the beginning are named Azoic, Archeozoic, Proterozoic, Paleozoic, Mesozoic and Cenozoic. We shall not be concerned with the first three eras, for early in that time there was no life on earth, and when it first began no plants or animals produced hard parts which could be fossilized. Our story is about the latter three.

Shortly after William Smith began his fossil hunting, a second child made an important contribution to the fossil story. Her name was Mary Anning. Living in the south of England, she helped her father collect fossil sea shells which they sold to tourists. When she was twelve years old Mary came on something much bigger than a shell; it was the fossilized skeleton of a large reptile that apparently had lived in the sea. This was in 1811 and no one up to that time had seen such a relic of prehistoric life. Later scientists called it Ichthyosaurus. You will read about it in a later chapter. Mary became a serious hunter of fossils and in 1821 she discovered the skeleton of another sea monster, Plesiosaurus, which created great excitement among scientists. Still another of her outstanding discoveries was the skeleton of a flying reptile now known as a pterodactyl.

For a while, even after scientists became seriously interested in fossils, most "finds" were made accidentally. They would turn up in a quarry, in excavations for buildings, in roadbed construction. But soon it became evident where good hunting grounds might be found. First of all, fossils have to be in sedimentary rocks (never in igneous or metamorphic) such as limestone, slate and shale, for these are composed of small bits of sediment pressed together. Also the sedimentary rocks would need to have been cut through by rivers or worn by other erosion, exposing a section of the rock layer. In such a situation a fossil hunter may explore until he finds some sign of fossils such as bits of bone or shells or footprints. Then it is worth while to dig.

The equipment used by a fossil hunter may not seem very impressive—at least not until we know how the various articles are put to use. "Tools" include an ordinary whisk broom, paintbrush, hammer, pickax, an awl for making holes, shellac, tissue paper, string, shovels, plaster of paris and burlap. Sometimes more impressive items are added, such as dynamite, for it often becomes necessary to knock down large masses of rock that cover the fossils. But often pick and hammer are all that are necessary for the heavy work. After this has been completed, the awl and brush are put to work clearing sand and dust from the fossil. By then the explorer is able to decide pretty surely how large and complete is the skeleton he has discovered.

As the bones or shells are uncovered, they must be given a coat of shellac and covered with tissue paper. Something that has been buried for perhaps many millions of years, when dug up and exposed to the air, is likely to crumble to dust unless this precaution is taken. As a further protection, each part of the skeleton is covered with strips of burlap that have been dipped in flour paste or in liquid plaster. When these dry, they hold the skeleton, or parts of it, so firmly that it may be moved without danger of breaking.

Next the bottom of the fossil must be given the same protective treatment the top and sides have received. If the specimen is very large, sticks of wood are attached to it in the fashion of splints. It is then ready to be packed in a wooden crate, padded with straw and shipped to museum laboratories.

Collecting fossil bones

One extremely important job a paleontologist does while collecting fossil bones is to make a chart that shows every bone, sketched just as it was found and given a number. This chart is of great help in the laboratory where the piecing together of a skeleton suggests the working out of a great jig-saw puzzle.

The first operation in the laboratory is to remove the burlap and plaster that were put on in the field. Then the fossils must be chipped free from any rock that surrounds them. Now a careful study begins as the experts judge to what part of an animal each bone belonged. Some may be considered sufficiently important to go on exhibition in a hall of prehistoric life; many will be put in storage for future study and reference.

A skeleton that is chosen for exhibition may need a tremendous amount of work. After the bones have been carefully placed together, iron rods must be bent to support them and fastened together to make a frame upon which the skeleton is braced. The finished exhibit shows the ancient animal's internal structure in a natural pose, with the iron supports well hidden. If a skeleton is not complete, but is nevertheless considered of special importance for exhibition, scientists must decide the size and shape of the missing bones. These are then reproduced in plaster so that the skeleton will be seen as a complete structure. When such substitution is necessary, however, a label on the exhibit mentions the parts that are man-made. Generally they are tinted to contrast with the real bones.

So much for the story of a single skeleton. It is a long and complicated one but, even so, is only one small part of the tremendous project of discovering the truth about prehistoric life. Scientists carefully study each fossil, comparing it with many other fossils. They write descriptions and opinions of their discoveries which are published in technical journals, and they work with a scientifically trained artist to produce illustrations. On occasion the paleontologist may work with the artist on a painting to be exhibited in the museum, along with the skeleton. Again much comparing is done: the fossil is checked against any related animals—living or extinct. Scientist and artist, with a thorough understanding of anatomy, decide how muscles and flesh once covered the bones that have been "brought back to life." One of the great artists in this field, Charles R. Knight, wrote: "Personally I never think of a fossil animal as being dead, but always picture it in my mind's eye as alive —an animated, breathing, moving machine which stands, walks, fights, or otherwise conducts itself after the fashion of a living creature."

There are a few instances of prehistoric life being preserved in a more complete form than fossil skeleton; occasionally a whole animal—flesh, skin and bone —was preserved in a frozen state. Bodies of great mammoths that perhaps fell into icy crevices have been discovered in Alaska and Siberia deeply buried

23

in the tundra. Nature, hundreds of thousands of years before the "quick-freeze" was hailed as a new invention, so preserved some of the mighty ancestors of modern animals.

Thus by fossil remains and frozen remains, by printed word and picture, and by reconstructed skeletons, we are given a glimpse into the long-distant past. As many bones are pieced together to form a single fossil skeleton, so a great number of these separate "glimpses" may be pieced together—and we have the thrilling story of the development of life from its beginnings, when the earth was young, to modern times.

Chapter II

THE EARTH'S FIRST CITIZENS

For the first signs of prehistoric life we must look backward about five hundred and fifty million years. Our planet, earth, was not really new by then. For millions of years it had been whirling in space and following an orderly path around the sun, but much of it was in a molten state and such rocks as had formed were barren, supporting no kind of life whatever. At first there was only a thin veil of atmosphere to shield it from the sun and as a result it was baked by day and frozen by night. After rock began to harden, the surface frequently opened and floods of lava poured forth from the cracks. With the outpourings came water vapors, and these were added to a slowly developing atmosphere. At last a point was reached where the atmosphere contained more moisture than it could hold, and dense clouds became rain.

Rain was the "curtain raiser" for the earth's exciting future, even though the first waters must have dried up as quickly as sprinklings on a hot stove. Rains fell in torrents, and for years; and after a while they carved out holes in which pools could form. Then brooks, rivers and finally great seas developed.

An earth made up of land areas and oceans begins to seem familiar to us, but there were still vast differences from the sea and land of today. The ancient seas were at first fresh water, rather than salty (the salt came gradually as a part of the sediment washed down from the land), and some shallow portions almost completely covered the continent of Asia, about half of the United States and more than half of Australia. But at last the stage was set for life to make its appearance; the shallow bodies of water proved the right sort of breeding grounds for tiny organisms.

Very often people think of the amoeba as being the simplest organism ever to exist, but in the beginning there was something still simpler. The earliest characters to enter the drama of life on earth were probably the minute structures known to science as Protista—a word taken from the Greek *protistos*, meaning "the very first." Not only were Protista extremely simple in structure, they could not definitely be classed as animal or plant but had some of the qualities of both these forms of life.

More time passed, and the very first forms developed into two definite groups of life—animal and plant. In the animal realm it is probable that among the first creatures were some much like the amoeba.

As anyone knows who has watched this little organism under a microscope, the amoeba has no front or back end. It is a jelly-like blob, composed of a single cell, and it reproduces itself by dividing into two parts. Scientists have an especial interest in the amoeba and certain other simple organisms of our modern world because they seem to contribute an important chapter to the story of the past. When life first began, almost no fossil records were left because animals were completely soft-bodied. But simple organisms such as the amoeba tend to remain unchanged through time and it is therefore felt that they give us a quite accurate picture of the earliest animals.

In time there came another period of development (the beginning of the Paleozoic era), when some creatures began to create protection for themselves in the form of hard coverings which later became true shells. This was the beginning of the type of animals such as oysters and clams that today are popularly known as "shellfish," though they are really not fish at all. They are without backbones and therefore are properly called invertebrates. The first part of the Paleozoic era is often referred to as the Age of Invertebrates.

There was great difference in form and size in the various invertebrates, though most of them had shells of one kind or another. Most outstanding of them all were the trilobites. They are not given this rating because they were the largest or most impressive in appearance; trilobites are considered so successful

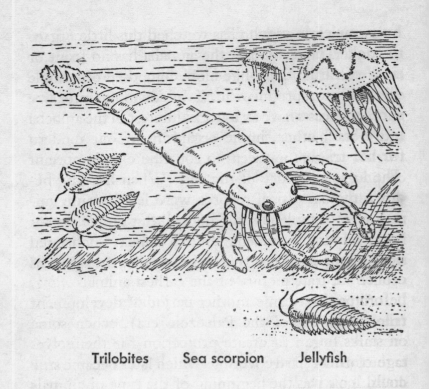

Trilobites   Sea scorpion   Jellyfish

because for many millions of years they dominated the earth scene. Fossil discoveries show that at least two thousand different varieties lived in widely scattered parts of the earth. The largest kind measured two feet in length, but the majority were no more than one and a half to three inches in length. The trilobites varied in habits as they did in size but there were some features that were alike in all.

The word "trilobite," meaning "three-lobed fossil," refers to the fact that the upper surface of the creature—a shell—was divided into three distinct parts by two clearly marked furrows running from front to back. The body also was divided into three sections of head, thorax and tail, and the thorax was divided into sections which could move against one another. Because of this, the trilobite could roll itself into a ball beneath its protecting shell. Other reasons for the trilobites' success were their eyes and legs. The legs, sometimes many pairs of them, ran right down the underside of the body. Each was divided into two parts, one suitable for walking, the other for swimming. Spines which projected from the inner sides of the legs served as jaws: the trilobite would crouch on top of its prey and "chew" with its legs before passing the food forward to the mouth. The trilobite's eyes were sometimes held up from the head on stalks, but even if they did not have the advantage of this elevation, they were slightly raised and could look backwards, sideways or upward. A pair of feelers at the front of the head detected food on the sea floor.

It is quite certain that the trilobites ate various kinds of food. Some may have lived entirely on a meat diet, preying upon small creatures such as worms; others doubtless found nourishment in seaweed and decaying vegetable matter. Some spent their lives buried in the sea floor, extracting their food from the mud. These burrowers after a while lost the use of their eyes. A growing trilobite lived through periods of especial danger when its protective shell became too tight and had to be shed. The shell would split at the head, allowing the soft-bodied inhabitant to creep forth. Now at the mercy of all flesh-eaters, it would lie quietly among the sea-weed until a new shell had formed.

Trilobites are classed as arthropods, or "creatures with jointed feet." Today the arthropods are represented by such animals as lobsters, centipedes and scorpions.

Another arthropod known only through fossils was the sea scorpion named eurypterid. Although eurypterids may not be so popularly known as the trilobites, they were more spectacular in appearance. Some were nine feet long! They had oar-like limbs which suggest that they could swim efficiently, and one species had a tail which apparently served as a rudder.

Although a nine-foot length sounds tremendous for an inhabitant of the early invertebrate world, the sea scorpion was surpassed in size by a cephalopod which grew a shell more than fifteen feet long and ten inches in diameter at its widest point. The word "cephalopod" means "head-foot" and is suitable to this type of creature because it had tentacles surrounding its mouth which gave the appearance of arms and feet. And actually they were used not only for grasping food but for crawling and swimming. A cephalopod's head which boasted the tentacle-surrounded mouth and big eyes, projected from the large end of the great shell. Two sharp beaks on the mouth enabled the huge animal to crack even the hard shell of a tribolite, so it had little trouble finding food. The shells of early cephalopods were straight, though later they grew curved and still later became coiled. These creatures were very early examples of jet propulsion, for they took water into the body to shoot it out through a tube on the underside of the head. As a result the cephalopod would be suddenly and swiftly propelled backward.

Cephalopods were mollusks, the group of animals to which clams, oysters and snails belong. Members also of the mollusk tribe are the octopus and squid found in our oceans today. They do not have shells but they suggest very strongly those gruesome undersea hunters of early days, cephalopods.

Far smaller creatures, but with just as large a name, were echinoderms, which adorned the early seas. "Adorn" may seem an odd word to use in connection with animals; however, many echinoderms because of their shape and coloring could easily have been mistaken for beautiful flowers. The name means "creatures with spiny skins" and it is applied today to such familiar living creatures as the sea star (or starfish) and sea urchin. In the early days before true fishes came into being the outstanding echinoderms were crinoids. "Sea lilies," the popular name for crinoids, indicates that this was indeed a flower-like animal. It was distinctly divided into a stem, attached at one end to the sea floor, and branching arms which looked like colorful petals. These waved to and fro in the water, capturing tiny organisms for food. For

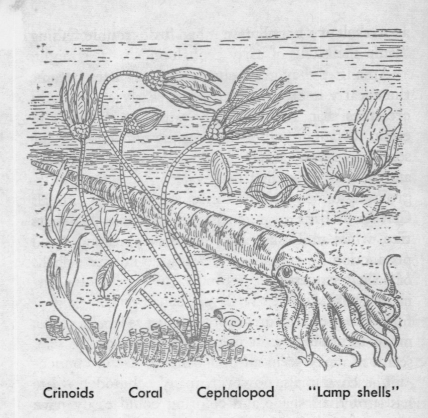

Crinoids   Coral   Cephalopod   "Lamp shells"

some millions of years crinoids were so numerous that scientists sometimes refer to that period of time as the "Age of Sea Lilies."

A far more complicated form of life than crinoids existed in the group of animals known as brachiopods. They were small—seldom more than two inches across—but had distinct digestive and nervous systems, kidneys, reproductive organs and strong muscles. The skeleton of certain brachiopods consisted of two shells, which resembled a Roman lamp;

as a result we know these now fossilized animals as "lamp shells."

Among the remarkably hardy forms of life in these early seas were the sponges—those amazing creatures that still abound in warm waters of our earth. When they first appeared they represented something new in animal structure, for they are among the first examples of a great number of cells grouping together and functioning as one organism. Certain of the cells absorb food, others are protective, while still others have the responsibility of reproduction. A whip-like mechanism inside the colony of cells draws in streams of water through the pores in its walls, then sends them out again. As food is filtered out of this water, the sponge has no need to move about; it is one of the flower-like animals that seems rooted to a certain spot.

The coral is another colony-type creature which has survived from the Age of Invertebrates to the present. As they do today, the coral polyps in those ancient seas secreted protective limestone. Some types grew together, forming massive branching or dome-shaped colonies. It is such skeletons that form the great reefs of tropical seas. And such skeleton formations sometimes are excellent fossil-hunting grounds, where millions-of-years-old coral-formed limestone has been lifted high and dry by the shifting earth.

Certain other animals of the Age of Invertebrates, though delicate in appearance and unprotected by hard coverings, also have survived to the present day.

Outstanding among them are jellyfish, those transparent, umbrella-shaped "blubbers" that often make themselves unpopular with swimmers. Their numerous tentacles are covered with sting cells, and bumping into one is a disagreeable experience. Sea anemones such as you may find in rock pools or beneath overhanging rocks along the shore were also a part of the underwater scene of that long-ago time, before life existed on land.

It may be rather surprising to realize that there were so many familiar inhabitants of our world in the early days of animal life. So much has completely changed since then! However, the countless things that were *not* in that far distant underwater world make a big difference between past and present. So far as fossil records reveal, until the period of time known as the Silurian, more than three hundred million years ago, there was no such thing as an animal with a backbone!

Chapter III

FISHES GROW ARMOR

The appearance of a backbone in certain kinds of creatures was more than a development, it was a revolution. Let us see some of the great contrasts between the vertebrates and the invertebrates. A vertebrate's type of skeleton makes a body more mobile and promotes a highly organized nervous system. And as a new type of skull evolved in the vertebrates, space was provided for a brain, thus making possible a higher degree of intelligence. The first backbones, therefore, were the beginnings of a kind of animal that did not have to depend for survival entirely on strength or on the protection of shells. Now brain power and speed, in varying degrees, had to be reckoned with!

Though millions of years later we can appreciate all these advantages, it would have taken a tremendous imagination to realize the possibilities in the very earliest vertebrates. There is a sea creature known as

35

amphioxus living today which gives a fairly good idea of what the vertebrate pioneers were like. Amphioxus has no real fins, no jaws, no skeleton, no ears or eyes. Its name means "sharp at both ends" and it is indeed shaped like a small, flattened cigar. Its great asset is a slim rod of gristle, called a notochord, which runs the length of its body and supports the soft parts, providing a strong axis on which the muscles can pull. Another extremely primitive vertebrate living in modern times is the lamprey—an eel-like creature which, like amphioxus, does not have jaws. It feeds by fastening itself to bodies of fish and sucking their flesh. Its "skeleton" is composed of not only a notochord but the suggestion of a true backbone.

Apparently in the Silurian period there were a number of creatures constructed on the notochord

Coccosteus, an armored fish

pattern, but not many have been preserved in fossil form. However, there also appeared on the scene vertebrates whose "skin" was actually bone, and many of these were preserved as fossils. The group as a whole are named ostracoderms which may be translated as "shell-skinned." In a number of features they resembled the lamprey. One type had no jaws; its mouth consisted of a crosswise slit or a small hole, and the entire front of the body was covered with a bony structure—a sturdy coat of armor. Only the tail and a bit of the rear part of the body were free for swimming.

Some of the armor was fantastic. Bony horns might project from the plating which covered the head. One kind (known as Cephalaspis, or "shield head") wore a large flattened, crescent-shaped plate of bone covering the forepart of its body, while rings of jointed bone encased the rest of it. Another type was not only covered with solid plates of bone on head and body but had thick, rounded scales on its tail. It also was equipped with two bone-covered fins with which it could push itself along on the mud, for although armor had definite advantages in giving protection, it must have been a serious handicap in swimming. Very likely the "boneheads" spent most of their time wriggling over the floor of the fresh-water lakes and streams in which they lived, grubbing for worms and other small animals to eat. The fact that the mouth was placed underneath the head indicates this.

Cephalaspis

Then there came an ostracoderm which was smaller and less heavily armored than the others. Its shape was more rounded than flat, and its mouth was at the front of the head rather than underneath. Here is evidence that this fish probably ventured away from mud-grubbing to try its luck in the open waters above. One kind in particular must have closely resembled some of our common fish of today, except that it had an odd ridge of hard spines along its back.

A feature of notable importance that developed in certain of the early fish was jaws. Without these an animal was definitely limited in its food possibilities. But when a fish had jaws that could open and close on victims, and then developed teeth with which to chew, it was really equipped for successful living.

Perhaps the biggest news of all from the Age of Fishes (or Devonian period), when the underwater boneheads were flourishing, was when certain types began to develop a new method of obtaining oxygen from the air. In addition to gills they used an air bladder, and in time this arrangement was further developed until there existed certain fishes that had not only gills but lungs as well. From them were to be produced the first land-living vertebrates—creatures that belonged to the two realms of water and land. Creatures that could live out of water as well as in it had a tremendous advantage.

When we think about "life" on our earth, it is usually the animals that first come to mind. However, if we stop to realize that there could be no animals without plant life on which to feed, the kingdom of the plants assumes equal importance and interest. As we have already discovered, the very first kinds of life on earth really could not be classed as plant or animal. Then life became more complex; there were distinct animals and distinct plants. But the pattern followed by plants and animals was similar: both spent long ages living only in the water before undertaking the daring step of venturing a life on the land.

Until the Silurian period, when animals with backbones first appeared, the only plants known to have lived were algae—plants that had no true leaves, stems or roots. The algae of ancient times included a great variety, even as we find in the algae group today. Some are microscopic bits of life, some are gigantic seaweeds more than a hundred feet long. One prehistoric seaweed has been discovered which had stems nearly two feet in diameter. When the first fossil remains of this "weed" were found, it was guessed that they were trunks of coniferous trees! However, later discoveries and studies confirmed for many scientists the fact that it had actually been a seaweed. Doubtless it was hundreds of feet long. It has been given the name Nematophycus. There must have been a tremendous variety of seaweeds in those early times, possibly representing three families of algae in existence today—the blue-green, green, and red algae. Their "remains" usually are in the form of shiny black film on the surface of hard shale.

To picture the dramatic developments when plants began a conquest of the earth, we should have an idea of how land and sea areas were shaping up about the close of the Silurian period and the beginning of a new period—the Devonian. By this time many regions had leveled off into flat land surfaces, and low coastal bays were bordered by broad marshes. These were regularly covered and uncovered by tides. Often these areas must have been blanketed with the abundant seaweeds, some of which had developed tiny, flat, somewhat leaf-like organs. As these were exposed to air when stranded by outgoing tides they would roll up, but if water washed over them before they died, they opened again. Gradually some of them became less dependent upon water and were able to live longer and longer in the air until they were actually land plants. They still had big adjustments to make, however. Roots had to be developed, for they had been accustomed to taking all their nourishment from the water in which they floated. At first they could only lie flat on the ground, but gradually a strengthened "cuticle" began to hold them upright and this in turn became a woody stem. Slowly but surely the delicate, slender leaves grew sturdy and developed breathing pores which served as the important means of communication between air and plant. A link between past and present becomes well established when we realize that certain reproduction steps of these early Devonian land plants could take place only in water, and this fact is true also of many of their modern descendants.

It is likely that we who are accustomed to the color and fragrance of flowers would find little beauty in the land plants of Devonian times. In the early and middle part of the period they were small and bare. The name Psilophyton given to one type seems appropriate to many, for the word means "naked plant." Fossils show it to have been about two feet high, with a woody stem about half an inch in diameter which grew out of a mass of creeping stems and rootlets. The upright stems were forked and bore ugly spines, and spores (a primitive type of seed) developed on some of these. Many other land plants came into being, all very much on the order of the "naked plant." And gradually another, more graceful type of plant came into existence. It was the beginning of ferns. There also appeared a variety of tree which was covered with overlapping leaf-like scales. Some of this type were small, others more than forty feet tall. There were odd smooth-stemmed plants with needle-like spines and a few primitive horsetail rushes.

As the Devonian period advanced, there came into existence several species of wonderful tree-like ferns. The continent of North America seems to have been particularly rich in these, and it was in New York State that a historic discovery was made concerning them. Rocks were being blasted for a great dam to be constructed when the workmen were startled to see a "fossil forest." There stood hundreds of fossilized tree trunks, still upright, just where they had been for hundreds of millions of years! The living forest apparently had been flooded and destroyed by the sea, which at that time reached up to the north.

This ancient forest aroused such great interest that it was given a very special exhibition. Much of the excavated material, including about forty stumps and trunks, was taken to the State Museum in Albany, New York. Here scientists and artists prepared full-sized models of the trees as they must have looked when living, to stand by the fossil stumps, and behind this they set a background scene showing all the graceful tree ferns and other species that flourished in Devonian days. Thus the State Museum boasts among its exhibits what may well be the oldest fossil forest in the world.

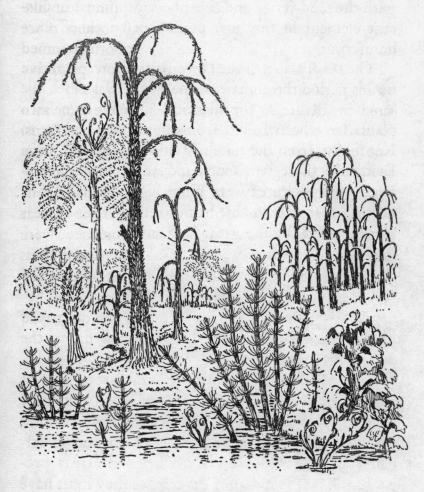

Devonian forest scene

Perhaps the most interesting single fact about the fossil forest is one type of tree, with slender, tapering trunk, furrowed bark and countless little leaflets. This tree did not depend on spores to reproduce itself but actually bore seeds—which puts it in a class with the seed-ferns, and these became a most important element in the next period, often called Carboniferous.

The fossil plants of the Devonian period reveal that in this period the climate of the world was much the same in all areas, for identical or closely related plants have been found from the Arctic regions to Kentucky, from the state of Ohio to eastern Russia. Evidently there was much moisture in the atmosphere, temperatures were quite high, and no frosts occurred. It was in this balmy setting that animals were readied for the great land invasion.

Chapter IV

ANIMALS TAKE TO THE LAND

Let us look now at an assortment of odd-looking animals bearing odd-sounding names.

There is Cacops, a thick-bodied creature about sixteen inches long with short, crooked legs and a stubby tail.

There is Eryops, also thick-bodied but much larger than Cacops, with a body length of about six feet, a broad flattened head and long tail.

There is Diplocaulus, a real freak, with a broad flat body and skull and eyes set close together on the upper surface of its bony head.

Though these may have the appearance of stupid, ungainly creations they hold an important spot in the history of animals, for they were among the first to flourish on dry land. Before them, as we have seen, certain fishes had developed to a point where they had lungs. Some also had an extra breathing mechanism, known as an "air bladder," which made it possible for them to gulp in air through the mouth. This added to the supply of oxygen that was brought in through the gills. As a result, when a long drought caused lakes and streams to dry up, fishes so equipped could survive until rain came again.

Then another feature was added to the ever-increasing aids for land living. This was the "lobe fin." On the fishes so equipped were two pairs of fringe-like fins each attached to a thick base, or lobe. The lobes were controlled by strong muscles, suggesting that the fins may have been used in the fashion of very primitive legs. The lobe-finned type of fish was not large. It had a blunt head covered with thick, bony plates and rows of bony scales along its body. Its backbone extended to the end of its tail, an arrangement found in the skeleton of sharks today. With sharp hard teeth it snapped up other fish—often young members of its own family—for food.

And at last there came a time, about three hundred million years ago, when certain fishes struggled out of the water on their sturdy lobe fins. At first this venture may have been to find more abundant water because the lake or stream in which they had lived was becoming dry. But as the "lobe fin" became increasingly successful on its overland journeys, it may have experimented with eating along the way, and so was able to make longer and more leisurely expeditions. As hundreds, thousands, perhaps millions of years passed, the muscular lobes became longer and could be rightfully considered legs, while the membranes that had joined the small bones at the end of the fins disappeared. The result of this alteration was claw-tipped toes.

Having reached a stage where they could walk rather than swim, wriggle or crawl, and where they could take all needed oxygen directly from the air, it would seem these creatures had entered on a completely new way of life. Yet such was not the case. Still they had to return to water to lay their eggs, and their young spent their infancy in water, breathing through gills. Thus became established the interesting class of animal which we know as "amphibian"—a word meaning "double-living." We use it today as a descriptive name for frogs and toads, salamanders and newts.

Once established in their double-life habits, the amphibians flourished. Some were sluggish and stayed close by muddy ponds while others became more swift-moving and even were able to scamper up tree trunks. In size they ranged from an inch long to a monstrous ten feet. Some wore overlapping scales or a more simple type of armor, but some developed the type of naked skin which covers modern frogs and toads. The usual shape of the head was broad and flat, with a wide frog-like mouth, but some heads were long and pointed. All had tails, all had external nostrils and external ears (though not with any part projecting from the head)—the first such hearing aids in the history of animals.

There was another "first" in animal life that ties

in with the external ear: for the first time in the world's history, animals could utter vocal sounds. Doubtless it was only a dismal croaking but it must have been sensational in the vast stillness of those days before there were birds to sing, and mammals to roar, howl, cry and talk.

One feature which these early amphibians possessed, though it did not survive, was a small gland situated on the head between the eyes. It somewhat resembled a third eye. Though apparently it was a light receptor of some sort, what its function may have been is not clearly understood. Gradually it withered away; nevertheless such a gland was in the make-up of many reptiles for long periods of time, and still today is found in many lizards.

It was to this weird group of early amphibians that Cacops, Eryops and Diplocaulus belonged. Ca-

Cacops

Diplocaulus

cops was a thick-bodied creature, less than a foot and a half long. It hatched from a small egg and grew through a polliwog stage. As an adult it still retained a tail and its legs were short, but it had an imposing trimming of lumps of bone down its back, and its jaws were equipped with many sharp enamel-covered teeth.

Eryops looked much like an overgrown Cacops, though its tail was longer in proportion to its body. Diplocaulus, however, was of quite a different pattern—and one of the strangest creations of all time. Its flat skull was extended backward on both sides and ended in points. Its legs were so weak as to be useless, and Diplocaulus apparently spent its whole life in the water, breathing through gills that were

Dimetrodon, one of the early reptiles which lived in the days of Eryops and other huge amphibians

covered by folds of skin and situated just behind its head.

As the animal kingdom went along with its successes and failures, the plant world was flourishing to an amazing degree by the Carboniferous period. Many still depended on spores to reproduce themselves but an ever increasing number developed true seeds. Today all of our typical flowering plants are seed-bearers, while in our ferns we find spore method still in use.

The giant plants of the Carboniferous time were club-moss trees, known as lycopods. There were two main types. One type grew to tremendous heights, possibly well over a hundred feet. The lower part of the trunk was straight and slender, and covered with scale-like leaves. At more than three quarters of its entire length from the ground, the trunk divided into an artistic array of branches. There were no small twigs such as are characteristic of our trees today, but numerous leaves stemmed directly from the branches as well as the trunks. Spore-bearing cones grew at the tips of the branches.

The second type of lycopod had a shorter, broader trunk and it was less commonly branched. Leaves covered the entire trunk, growing larger and more impressive toward the top.

Other remarkable trees important in Carboniferous times were the cordaites—forerunners of our own coniferous firs and pines. They were graceful as well as tall, some attaining heights of a hundred and fifty feet. The leaves were four, five or even six feet long, but were rather slender and stiff and formed a luxuriant crown atop the branchless trunk.

The handsome horsetail trees called calamites, which had come into existence long before, were flourishing. By this time they had giant thirty-foot stems, segmented somewhat like bamboo, with slen-

51

der leaves encircling the joints. Calamites did not develop spores but depended for reproduction on new plants branching from a spreading underground stem.

Because of their size the lycopods, cordaites and calamites seem to dominate the Carboniferous scene. However, ferns of all sorts and shapes far outnumbered them, forming the dense undergrowth which in time was to harden into layers upon layers of coal. Strangely enough (since our modern fern are spore-bearers), some species of this early time produced seeds.

As we, today, find tropical foliage good breeding grounds for insects, so the fern forest of Carboniferous times proved a suitable setting for the development of the first insects. According to fossil records, the six-legged tribe put in appearance soon after amphibians had become established. Before them, too, there had developed such insect-like creatures as spiders, scorpions and centipedes. But soon it was the insects that were of first importance. Not only was there a great variety of species—more than a thousand are known to have existed as the Carboniferous period came to a close—but their size was amazingly large compared with the common insects of today.

All in all the earth must have taken on a rather settled look by the Carboniferous, covered as it was with rich green vegetation and many forms of life creeping, walking and even flying about it. But actually it was far from being a "finished product." Changes gradually but constantly were taking place, as in the Northern Hemisphere where earth movements were slowly raising former sea beds into swampy plains. The lush Carboniferous period—after eighty-five million years—was coming to an end.

Now with an increased degree of earth activity the Permian period was ushered in. The great Appalachian range was pushed up, not as we know it, but with extremely high, jagged peaks. In Russia the mighty Ural range made its appearance. On our own west coast there was tremendous volcanic activity. Some of these changes in turn altered the course of ocean currents and were partly responsible for changes in local climates. Besides, other widespread and drastic development were occurring in the world's weather. Frigid temperatures visited much of the earth while some regions baked until they became waterless deserts. During twenty-five million Permian years, plant and animal life were put to a severe test. Many large and imposing species disappeared but those that were adaptable carried life on into a new age and were rewarded when the climate became friendly again.

Chapter V

ALL SORTS OF DINOSAURS

One of the most eye-opening facts about the history of our earth is that every so often the big, successful-appearing creatures had to yield in importance to a smaller, less imposing kind of animal. One such case we find after the Permian period when not only a new period (the Triassic) but also a new era (the Mesozoic) began.

By way of introducing the newcomers in the Triassic period, let us look back a way to the time when amphibians had become well established and were flourishing. It was then that a somewhat different kind of creature began to emerge—one that had found the secret of being a complete "land-lubber." Like the amphibians, it produced its young from eggs but its eggs did not have to be laid in water. The new type of egg had a hard shell and a yolk to nourish the embryo. This latest model in animals was, of course, the reptile. Besides its advanced egg-laying habits, it was evolving a bone structure that was different in shape from that of the amphibians. This was especially noticeable at the neck and toes. In general it seems to have been fashioned somewhat on the plan of a crocodile, although the average length was no more than two feet.

When a new era dawned after the hardships of the Permian period, the reptiles had become important citizens of the world, and in a comparatively short time the amphibians were pushed into the background. This actually was the beginning of a stretch of a hundred and forty million years which is often called the Age of Reptiles, though it is really an era. The Triassic, Jurassic and Cretaceous are the three periods of which the Mesozoic era is composed.

When we hear of "prehistoric reptiles," the picture that comes to mind most quickly is one of giant, towering dinosaurs. So completely have these creatures captured the imagination of modern man that we see them in advertisements, comic books and even in movies. But many other reptiles—and even many dinosaurs—came before the giants. Some of the smaller dinosaurs were about the size of jack rabbits. In further variation, some of these reptiles walked on two feet while others went on all fours. Some lived on flesh (all the early ones did so); others were strictly plant eaters. Some wore heavy armor; some had no protective covering whatever.

The variety in size and shape of this one special class of reptile brings up a very natural question: Just what *is* a dinosaur?

To scientists the name "dinosaur" is a very general term. It may be applied to a large assortment of reptiles which are divided into two distinct groups and are set apart from other reptiles by certain characteristics. Therefore, as a descriptive word, it includes a great variety of prehistoric beasts; it may be compared for its generality with the term used for the many hoofed animals that we know as ungulates. Translated from its Greek origin, it means "terrible lizard." It was bestowed on some of the first dinosaur skeletons to be found and studied— not much more than a hundred years ago. These happened to be the large types and the adjective "terrible" seemed very suitable.

In the years that followed, remains were discovered of an ever increasing variety of prehistoric reptiles which had features that related them to dinosaurs. And it became an established fact that the dinosaurs could be divided into two groups—one having "reptile hips"; the other, "bird hips." In other words, the hipbones of some were arranged in a pattern typical of most reptiles, while in others the hipbones were set in an arrangement similar to a bird's pelvis.

In the Triassic period dinosaurs appeared in impressive numbers and in many parts of the earth. Eventually they were residents of every continent from the north of Europe to the southern tip of Africa, and from the western United States to eastern Asia. Possibly the most noted of all dinosaur-hunting grounds is an area of some 100,000 square miles, made up of portions of New Mexico, Utah, Wyoming, Alberta, Montana and Colorado. The remains of innumerable intriguing types—including some of the real giants—have been discovered in this region.

To appreciate the wonderful variety of dinosaurs that flourished during the Age of Reptiles, let us look at some of the most interesting kinds.

Though he was not one of the early ones (he lived in Cretaceous times) Tyrannosaurus rex seems to deserve first attention because of his size and might.

As the name "rex" suggests, this animal was a king in the animal world. (A complete translation of his name is "tyrant king of the dinosaurs.") His great size was impressive enough. As he stood erect on his enormous hind legs, his head was eighteen feet above the ground—he could comfortably look down on roofs of most modern houses—and his body was fifty feet long. But besides size, Tyrannosaurus had fierce teeth in four-foot, iron-strong jaws. A heavy tail not only served as a prop when he was resting and a balancing weight when he was in action, but was a mighty club when he was fighting.

Unhappily for all his neighboring creatures, Tyrannosaurus was a meat eater. In the swamplands and jungle-like country that covered part of the western United State some seventy million years ago, no animal was safe from his hungry raids—although those that spent much of their time in deep swamps suffered little persecution. The "tyrant king" needed firmer ground on which to tread. He could probably chase his victims with considerable speed, for even using a slow stride, each step with his enormous legs would cover many feet of ground. On his front legs, which looked like shriveled arms, were strong claws that could carry food to his waiting jaws. And here were teeth well suited to an animal tyrant king. Some were six inches long; they were double-edged and dagger-like!

Among the more helpless victims of Tyrannosaurus were the dinosaurs popularly known as the "duckbills," though their more scientific name is trachodonts. The duckbills were large. Standing on his hind feet, an adult was all of sixteen feet high and in length measured thirty feet. He was well supplied with teeth (the name "Trachodon" means "pavement tooth"); on each side of both jaws were rows of several hundred of them, arranged one on top of another. But the front of his mouth was expanded in a broad duck-like bill and was toothless. Hundreds of teeth and no chance to bite at Tyrannosaurus when he was attacked!

With this type of mouth it is clear that the duckbill dinosaurs lived on vegetable food. They appar-

Triceratops   Trachodon

ently swam well and spent much of their time in or near the water. The toes of their front feet were connected by skin, forming an actual webbing.

Because of one remarkable fossil discovery of Trachodon, we have quite certain knowledge of its type of skin. This seems to have been pebbled, somewhat like the surface of a golf ball. A "mummy," found in Wyoming, showed this ancient reptile in its entirety. Apparently it died under circumstances where the hot sun dried muscles and soft flesh before they could decay. The skin shrank, becoming hard and leathery, and though it did not become fossilized along with the bones, it left a perfect impression in the sandy clay on which it rested. This in time hardened into rock—bearing a permanent record detail of the Age of Reptiles.

Trachodon had some fantastic relatives. One type had an expansion of nose bones which gave it a beaked appearance. Another wore a divided crest atop its head; another was adorned with a gracefully curved crest. All had the broad "duckbills." The first dinosaur skeleton ever discovered and described in our own country was that of a duckbill dinosaur. It had been entombed in the marl beds not far from the city of Philadelphia.

Though Tyrannosaurus met no opposition from Trachodon or his relatives, it was a different matter with Triceratops. More than anything else this mighty creature resembled an army tank. His was a thick, squat, twenty-foot-long body, weighing perhaps ten tons, and his enormous head flared out in a great shield, protecting his neck and shoulders. On his nose was a stout horn, and over each eye was another long horn. His name, Triceratops, was suggested by three Greek words meaning "three," "horn" and "face."

Triceratops could use his horns to excellent advantage because of tremendous neck and leg muscles and a ball-and-socket joint by which his great skull was attached to his backbone. With this arrangement he must have been able to lower his head till

60

the long horns were directed at his enemy, then bring them into action with a powerful upthrust. However, except for defending himself against Tyrannosaurus and fighting against a rival male of his own kind, Triceratops was a peaceful fellow. He ate vegetation rather than preying on other animals.

The ancestor of Triceratops is among the most interesting of all dinosaurs—most interesting because of the remarkable fossil discoveries which show its development from egg and newly hatched baby to a fully grown adult. Its name is Protoceratops ("first horn face").

Protoceratops was not large, no more than five or six feet in length—but in proportion to this size it had a very big head. Besides its actual size, the skull extended back to form a frill that stood out over the neck and shoulders. The front of its face formed a parrot-like beak, on top of which grew a small bump that was the beginning of a horn.

Besides the frill and the nose "bump," Protoceratops did not seem especially impressive. It had short legs, and it probably almost crawled on its belly as it walked. However, this small dinosaur made history in the world of science by leaving its complete life story in fossil form. Several nests of its eggs were discovered in the desert sands of Mongolia, and as they were the first complete dinosaur eggs ever to be found they made headline news. They were several inches in length, and in shape and covering they resembled the eggs laid today by lizards or crocodiles. In each of two of the eggs there was a fossilized unhatched partial embryo of a baby Protoceratops. Carrying the life story on from there, a series of skulls revealed the growth of this reptile, not only in size but in the possession of the bone frill at the back of its skull. The baby had no such feature—it developed gradually. And as millions of years went by, descendants of this ungainly creature boasted ever greater frills and ever fiercer horns until the mighty Triceratops was created.

If Triceratops is comparable to an army tank, another type of dinosaur may well be considered a super-armored tank. This group was composed of Ankylosaurus and his close relatives. On them a real

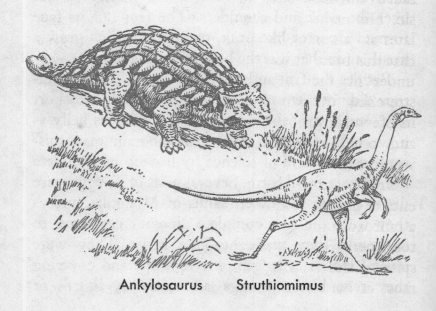

Ankylosaurus   Struthiomimus

armor of bony plates covered the entire body, head and tail. Ankylosaurus had a low, squat body. He was of medium size for a dinosaur, and lumbered about on all fours in his search for plant food with little concern for Tyrannosaurus or other meat eaters. His strong armor was enough to baffle the most dagger-like teeth. And if some creature prompted more by hunger than good sense tried to attack him, Ankylosaurus had only to swing his heavy, plated tail which ended in a great club-like mass of bone. No meal would be worth contact with such a weapon!

To find the dinosaur that is the delight of many artists and designers of comic cartoons we must go back to an earlier period than that in which Ankylosaurus and these other great reptiles lived—the Jurassic. His name is Brontosaurus—a word that translates as "thunder lizard," and was meant to suggest that this beast was so enormous the earth thundered under his feet. However, this is probably over-stretching the imagination, for Brontosaurus spent its life wading in the shallow parts of rivers and lakes and other swampy regions where "thundering" would not be very likely.

Brontosaurus was enormously long—some seventy or eighty feet from nose to tip of tail. (As long as a railroad engine!) And he doubtless weighed many tons, perhaps almost as much as eight elephants. In spite of this bulk he was a graceful figure because most of his length was made of an extremely long tail and neck. His head was small indeed for so enormous a creature. Eating must have been a full time job as he sought nourishment for a giant's body but had to bite and chew food with relatively small jaws. His teeth—spoon-shaped and even—reveal that he lived on plants.

Staying in swamps and shallows not only helped Brontosaurus keep away from fierce meat-eating dinosaurs, the water helped support him. Though his feet were broad and his legs looked sturdy, the joints were poorly formed. He must have felt quite "weak-kneed" when walking on solid earth.

A close relative, Diplodocus by name, also spent his days in fresh-water marshes and lagoons. In fact he was especially designed for watery surroundings in having nostrils placed on the top of the head so that he could breathe while he was almost entirely submerged.

Diplodocus was the longest of all dinosaurs. One skeleton in the Carnegie Museum at Pittsburgh, Pennsylvania, is eighty-seven feet in length! His slender neck was almost twice as long as his body, and ended in a ridiculously small head. He was not so bulky as Brontosaurus, but nevertheless his daily food requirements must have been enormous, especially as the vegetation in that distant time was not so rich in nutriment as our modern grains and fruits. Scientists have estimated that Diplodocus ate about seven hundred pounds of ferns and other greens every day!

Brontosaurus

Fancy and fascinating are the words to describe Stegosaurus, still another dinosaur of Jurassic times that lived both in America and in Europe. His fancy trimming consisted of a series of large triangular bony plates which grew upright in two rows down the middle of his back. Some of them were as high as two feet; they were thin and sharp-edged. It would seem the purpose of such a feature must have been protection for the creature's backbone. Certainly the plates could not have been useful as a weapon for attack. More practical were the four

Allosaurus, mighty flesh-eating dinosaur which was a neighbor of Brontosaurus

Stegosaurus

huge spikes at the tip of the tail that could be swung into action against an enemy. However, the bony plates rising along the back made Stegosaurus a truly impressive beast.

Spectacular though the plates are, Stegosaurus has made an even greater impression on dinosaur experts by his brain—or lack of it. Though this reptile was all of twenty feet long and weighed something like ten tons, his brain was no larger than a walnut. Here was an animal that surely "wouldn't know enough to come in out of the rain"! He would have fared badly indeed, even in the reptilian age, if he had not had an enlargement of the spinal cord in his hip. This was actually a nerve center that controlled the movements of the spiked tail and hind legs, but it has often given rise to humorous comments about the "second brain" of Stegosaurus. In fact it inspired the noted dinosaur verse by Bert Leston Taylor of the Chicago *Tribune* staff, which reads in part:

> *You will observe by these remains*
> *The creature had two sets of brains—*
> *One in his head (the usual place)*
> *The other at his spinal base. . . .*
>
> *If one brain found the pressure strong*
> *It passed a few ideas along.*
> *If something slipped his forward mind*
> *'Twas rescued by the one behind. . . .*

Leaving Stegosaurus, Brontosaurus and their neighbors to go back still further in time, to the Triassic period, we find the reptiles that were the ancestors of all these varied dinosaurs. These are known as thecodonts. There was considerable variety among them, but all were small, all walked on their two hind feet, all had a deep light skull, and all were meat eaters. The thecodonts were ancestors of other animals, too: birds, crocodiles and the flying reptiles about which we shall read later. But as we look at the general forms of all these creatures it is easiest by far to see the resemblance of dinosaurs—especially the flesh eaters—to great-great-grandfather Thecodont.

For many years after the first dinosaur remains had been discovered there was great curiosity as to how they produced their young. Since most reptiles lay eggs, it was supposed that dinosaurs had done so; but proof was lacking. Any doubts were cleared up eventually when dinosaur eggs were found—in France, Mongolia, Portugal, South Africa and in our own country. Some had very solid shells, some had shells that were almost paper-thin. Some were pebbled while others were smooth. They varied from four to nine inches in length. Evidently they were produced by various kinds of dinosaurs but none of them were giants. It has been estimated that a Brontosaurus egg might have been as large as a football.

These eggs that never hatched must have been suddenly cut off from air and the warmth of the sun, possibly by a windstorm blowing large amounts of sand over them. In time the shells cracked and, as the liquid ran out, it was replaced by sand which had been sifting through the shell. Thus the eggs kept their shape and eventually became rock, even as the loose sand above them was doing.

Chapter VI

INSECTS, FLYING REPTILES AND EARLY BIRDS

When we see a cat chase a bird and the bird escapes into the air, we appreciate keenly one of the advantages of flight. Safety for those who have the power! And we do not need actually to cross the continent by plane in a few hours to realize that travel in the air is swift and simple compared to making our way on solid earth. Man's flight by mechanical means is very recent indeed; birds having this ability date back millions of years. Before them were the flying reptiles, and long before their time certain insects had discovered the art of flight.

The six-legged creatures that we know as insects undoubtedly had their beginnings in some group of marine ainmals. They may have appeared a short time after the first land plants started to take hold, but the first actual fossil records of their existence are found in Carboniferous times. By the close of the Carboniferous period, however, they were abundant and flourishing. More than a thousand species have been traced to that time. Some were giants compared to our present-day insects; cockroaches were four inches long and dragonflies had a wingspread of well over two feet.

There is little evidence of insects early in the Age of Reptiles. Perhaps there was a setback in their development or, more probably, conditions were not right for their remains to become fossilized. But setback or no, by the middle of this era they were on the earth in ever increasing abundance. Not only the modern groups of dragonflies and cockroaches, but beetles, cicadas, grasshoppers, locusts, ants and termites were present. Some of these, as we know, became expert fliers, but of more importance to the world's future was the fact that many became partners with members of the plant world. An interdependence developed whereby insects obtained their food from plants and in so doing they conveyed pollen from one to another, thus insuring fertilization.

The Age of Reptiles was well advanced when a creature other than an insect attempted a conquest of the air. Apparently the first flying vertebrates—animals with backbones—appeared during the Jurassic periods, about a hundred and sixty million years ago.

The flying reptiles, like the dinosaurs, were descended from the thecodonts, but they followed a different line of development. Quite possibly it was their pursuit of insects which scrambled high up tall tree trunks that set their course. At first they crawled after the insects, but gradually they must have started leaping—first from a short distance up the trunk back to the ground, then longer and more daring leaps. In time the creatures that followed this practice developed a tough, flexible membrane which spread from the sides of the body to the limbs. Now they were equipped for actual gliding, much as our "flying" squirrel is, and could sail short distances between branches or even between trees. More time passed, and the size of the "wings" increased, as did the strength of the muscles which controlled them. Another adaptation for flight occurred as large cavaties came to exist in the skull, and the bones of the skeleton became hollow and filled with air. This made for extreme lightness; a flying reptile with a three-foot wing span probably weighed little more than half a pound.

The flying reptiles flourished for something like one hundred million years. In this time there were many varieties. Some were no larger than sparrows, some had a wingspread of twenty-five feet. Some had short tails, others had long thin tails tipped with flat "rudders." Some hunted by day, some by night. Their diet was probably made up of insects or insects and fish. The name by which they are known is pterosaurs (meaning "wing reptile").

Among the early pterosaurs was one that inhabited northwestern Europe. It was nearly a yard long

Pteranodon   Tylosaurus

and had a long narrow head. With a patch of wrinkled skin around each eye and long, sharp teeth, it must have been a real monstrosity. Still it would have been quite mild-appearing compared to the biggest flying reptile of them all, which lived long after. This was Pteranodon, which zoomed through the skies while dinosaurs roamed the land.

The head of Pteranodon was from six to seven feet long, with a great triangular crest or cap that was balanced by a long, toothless head. Though his body was no more than twenty-four inches in length his wings when spread measured twenty-five or more feet across. His skin was smooth and bare of feathers. As in all pterosaurs, each wing of Pteranodon was made of a thin sheet of skin that stretched from the the body and hind legs to the arms and to one long, thin finger.

This type of wing must not have been very practical, for if the thin piece of skin was torn, flight would be impossible. In contrast a bat's wing has the support of four fingers rather than two, and in birds the finger bones are closely bound together. If he lived today Pteranodon could not compete in flight with birds or bats because the operation of his wings was less efficient; but at gliding he would be a real champion. With that enormous wingspread and light body he must have been able to soar endlessly on air currents that rose from the warm tropical seas and land. A study of fossils found in the chalk beds of western Kansas reveals that this reptile cruised at least a hundred miles over the water.

However, Pteranodon doubtless was rather awkward and helpless on land. Possibly he rested on the knuckle joints of his closed wings, but since these joints could not move back and forth he must have been unable to walk on them. If he stood on his hind legs he would have had to hold up his giant wings. The solution to his problems probably lay in three hooked claws on the wing joints. With them he could hook onto rocks and hang on cliffs and trees. When ready to travel, he would simply push off into the air.

Like all pterosaurs, Pteranodon had a large brain—large, that is, for a reptile. He had a poor sense of smell but was favored with keen eyesight. This he needed to spot fish from high in the air.

Although fine fossil skeletons of Pteranodon have been found from western North America to Europe, scientists have discovered nothing about its babies or nests. Possibly it did not have the nesting habit at all —at least not in the sense birds do. Whatever its habits, this flying reptile and its relatives flourished for millions of years. It was only when the Age of Reptiles gave way to the Age of Mammals that they vanished from the earth, leaving no descendants.

But the end of the pterosaurs did not mean the end of flying vertebrates. About the time certain reptiles were beginning their daring experiment of flight, other descendants of the thecodonts were headed in the same direction. These were the birds. In the beginning there seemed to be little difference between a bird and a pterosaur. Both possessed true teeth, and the bird's skull and long tail were more reptilian than bird-like. However, there was one important difference: the bird had feathers. The skeleton of the first bird known to have existed was found in Germany, in rock formed during the Jurassic period. Science christened it Archaeopteryx, using the Greek word for "ancient wing." The skeleton might well have been mistaken for that of a reptile if the imprint of its feathers had not been clearly preserved on the stone.

Archaeopteryx was about the size of a crow. His head was unfeathered, but along the entire length of his forelimbs, feathers were well arranged to be of aid in flight. Another benefit of the soft feathery covering was that it helped to keep an even body temperature. This was of especial importance since changes had been taking place in the circulation system and in the structure of the heart which combined to make him "warm-blooded," so that his temperature did not vary with the changing temperatures of his environment. These elements worked together to give Archaeopteryx a great advantage over reptiles, for he could be more active and withstand changing temperatures better than a cold-blooded animal.

The teeth of this early bird were slanted backward, were widely spaced and sharp. They were

76

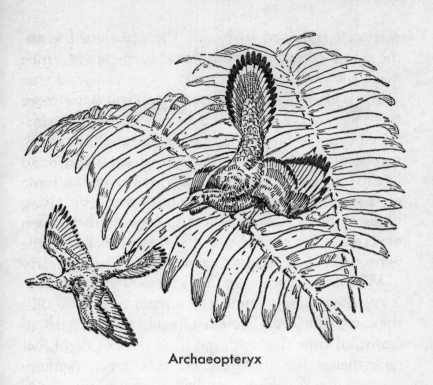

Archaeopteryx

good weapons for seizing and holding prey, but probably of little use in chewing. No bird living to-day can furnish us with a glimpse of how birds would look with jaws and teeth, for the jaws of Archaeoptryx in time gave way to a toothless beak. Probably much of his food was made up of insects and small reptiles which could be caught on the ground or by scrambling up trees and among the giant ferns. But there were the huge dragonflies to be caught, and no doubt the odd reptile-like bird many times tried out his wings in pursuit of them. When Archaeopteryx caught up with a victim he was well equipped to handle the situation, for on the tip of each wing were three sharp-clawed "fingers" for catching and tearing.

But with all his advantages for survival Archaeopteryx gave way, later in the Age of Reptiles, to different types of birds. There is a long gap in the fossil record of this branch of the animal kingdom; then in the Cretaceous period, somewhat before the time of Tyrannosaurus, several interesting and different types of birds made their mark. One of these, discovered in the chalk beds of Kansas, is called Hesperornis, which means "western bird."

With Hesperornis we find a strange situation that is repeated with a number of creatures throughout the earth's history. Though a member of the exalted feathered tribe that achieved the power of flight, he nevertheless was flightless. He was large, standing four or five feet high, and had a large head with a long beak. His was a streamlined body; there were not even wings to break the smooth line of his sides. His legs were so close to his tail that he must have been completely off balance if he tried to walk. Swimming was a different matter. He could paddle lazily through the water or, when hungry, could swim fast and purposefully after fish. In his beak-like jaws were ninety-four sharp teeth. He had no trouble dealing with his slippery prey!

There are two theories about the nesting habits of Hesperornis. These odd birds may have wriggled out on the shore and laid their eggs there, or they

78

may have built a floating nest of mud and dead plants which they attached to rushes in shallow water. No fossil eggs or nest of Hesperornis have ever been found.

Another fish-eating bird which enlivened the scene late in the Age of Reptiles was Ichthyornis. Though it sought its food in the water as Hesperornis did, Ichthyornis was a flying bird. It had well-developed wings, and in fact the bones of its wings and feet are extraordinarily like those of our modern birds. It was no more than nine inches long, and somewhat resembled the shore bird we know as a tern.

The fossil story of birds is incomplete for long stretches. The reason for this might be that the winged creatures used their flying ability to inhabit the highlands rather than competing with the reptiles about low-lying swamps and seashores. In the highlands rock was already being weathered away rather than being formed; as a result the remains of birds did not often leave their imprint in stone or harden into fossils. But we know from the number and variety of birds today that they flourished and became adapted to all kinds of conditions; in fact they are among the most adaptable of living things. They are found in arctic cold, in desert heat, on mountain heights and lowland. Some are remarkable long-distance fliers, others are completely flightless. They range in size from the tiny hummingbird to the huge ostrich.

Sometime during the Age of Reptiles birds seem to have undergone a number of important changes, exchanging teeth and jaws for horny beaks, replacing long jointed tails with a fan style, and fusing the fingers into wings, thus affording additional support. But with all the adjustments that took place, the birds held onto their most distinctive and valuable feature—feathers.

Chapter VII

IN ANCIENT SEAS

While animal history was being made on land, with reptiles increasing in size and power until they dominated the entire scene, there were lively developments, too, in the waters of the earth. Fishes of many kinds were flourishing. The sharks which dated back to Devonian times had progressed to the extent that some forms lived in the oceans and others roamed the fresh waters of lakes and rivers.

One of the most spectacular of the Devonian fish was the giant named Dinichthys. Dinichthys may be translated as "terrible" or "huge" fish, and it is a well-deserved name. Its skull, which measured over a yard in length, was equipped with jagged projections on the great jaws which served as teeth. Besides having this helpful equipment, Dinichthys was swift-moving and strong. One fossil discovery revealed a specimen that was apparently well over

81

forty feet in length. By the Carboniferous times that followed the Devonian, the giant Dinichthys apparently vanished, but there was an ever increasing variety in the fish population. Some of the newcomers were familiar forms, such as the skates and rays we know today.

Certain reptiles, descendants of creatures that left the water to be land-dwellers, were venturing back into the watery realms. Perhaps they found food more easily there; perhaps they were not in such danger from the flesh-eating dinosaurs. At any rate return to the water they did. This could not have been simple action, for they no longer were suited for life in watery realms. But gradually they learned to swim and some became as skillful as fishes in the art. In many cases the four short legs were transformed into flippers or paddles, while other types propelled themselves chiefly by a strong fish-like tail fin. It seems apparent that many produced living young, rather than going through the egg-laying process. However, in one important respect the reconverted land dwellers did not change; they continued to use lungs and to breathe air. Certainly for life in a watery habitat, gills would seem more efficient than lungs but "nature" did not go backward in this way. Animals that gave up certain physical equipment for a new kind of life had to alter their new equipment for survival in their original realm; they could not recapture the physical characteristics which they had made use of in the first place.

Even before the Age of Reptiles began, several kinds of primitive reptiles had begun turning back to the sea, but we must look to the reptilian age to find the really specatcular sea reptiles. Among the largest and most widely known are the ichthyosaurs or "fish reptiles." (You may remember reading in the first chapter about Mary Anning, the young girl who made the first discovery of the fossil remains of an ichthyosaur.) The ichthyosaur was streamlined from its pointed snout to its fish-like tail. Its limbs had become fin-like flippers and its body outline was quite similar to our modern porpoise. One large, fleshy fin along the back prevented the creature's rolling from side to side as it swam. Rows of sharp teeth lined its long jaws, and exceptionally large eyes were another distinctive feature.

Ichthyosaurs were large compared with modern reptiles (they grew from twenty to thirty feet long) but they were quite dwarfed by the huge plesiosaurs. This was another water-living type of reptile which lived in many parts of the world including the great inland sea that covered part of western North America. A typical plesiosaur, with barrel-shaped body and extremely long neck, might have measured up to fifty feet in length. Although both plesiosaurs and ichthyosaurs were reptiles that had become thoroughly adapted to life in the water, they were very different from each other in appearance and actions. Where ichthyosaurs were fish-like, plesiosaurs were not.

A plesiosaur had a broad, flattened body which was equipped with huge rowing paddles. In this it resembled the turtles. But, unlike turtles, it had a fairly long tail and an extremely long neck. While the "paddles" of the ichthyosaurs probably served merely as balancing aids, the plesiosaurs used theirs as oars. It is believed that they paddled themselves

Plesiosaurs   Ichthyosaurs

along the surface of the water or just beneath it, using powerful muscles and strong shoulder and hip girdles to propel their built-in paddles.

There were two types of plesiosaur, distinguished by differently shaped heads. One kind had a small, short head; the other's was long with a sharp beak. The small-headed type had a neck that was especially long but many of these water-living reptiles were favored with snake-like and flexible necks. So equipped, one could dart its head in any direction, catching up with unsuspecting fish while the great hulking body was still a distance away. The mouth would quickly open and the prey would be trapped; an abundance of long sharp teeth prevented any escape.

Between the fish-like ichthyosaurs and the somewhat turtle-like plesiosaurs, it might seem that the seas and large lakes had more than enough monsters late in the Age of Reptiles. But there were still others —rivals to dispute the supremacy of the waters with them. Notable among these were the mosasaurs. Like the others, they were land-living reptiles—actually lizards—that had turned to an aquatic way of life. Their name in translation suggests "sea lizard."

All the mosasaurs were large, but probably the most impressive was one that has been named Tylosaurus. This creature was as large as a medium-sized whale but its body was extremely flexible so that it swam with fish-like movements. As a further aid it had the paddle-shaped limbs that were adapted from walking legs and feet. The feature that gave Tylosaurus a really terrifying appearance was its tremendous mouth filled with rows of sharp-pointed teeth. As if they weren't big enough to begin with, the creature's jaws were hinged in the middle and could be bowed outward. With this arrangement the mouth could be opened to take in prey of amazingly large size.

For many years, every now and then seafaring people have reported seeing (always at a distance!) a sea serpent. Descriptions varied with different reporters but always the "serpent" was enormous, and in general appearance a cross between a mythical dragon and a snake. No proof has ever been established of the existence of such a monster in modern times, but Tylosaurus would well fit the description.

Among the sea creatures that had to be wary of the mighty Tylosaurus was the prehistoric turtle Archelon. As we picture the common turtles we know today, this kind of animal might not seem a very impressive kind of prey for the giant, but Archelon was a giant in its own right. Its broad shell alone measured over eight feet in length, its front flippers were six feet long and its head about thirty inches. Its shell was not really hard, however, merely tough and leathery. The vicious teeth of Tylosaurus would not have been stopped by any of the turtle's protective measures. A discovery of the fossil remains of one individual clearly shows that one of its hind feet had been bitten off.

Archelon

Archelon had good jaws of its own, ending in sharp-edged beaks which could crush and crunch very efficiently. Possibly the turtle's favorite food was fish but, unfortunately for its eating pleasure, many fish were far speedier and could not be caught. Usually Archelon had to be content with the small shelled creatures called ammonites and oysters.

When Archelon wasn't hunting, it spent long hours resting in the mud at the bottom of shallow waters. But besides eating and resting, there was another important function with which the female turtles were concerned: egg laying. Unlike some of the reptiles that had become water-living animals,

87

they did not keep their eggs in the body until the young hatched and then release living young into the water. Archelon retained the reptile habit of depositing eggs on the earth. To do so was not easy, for her weight was tremendous and her flippers designed for swimming rather than walking. Slowly and with great effort she pulled up on a beach and traveled over the sand until reaching a spot high enough to be safe from lashing waves. Here she started to dig, pushing and scooping sand until a large, shallow pit was formed.

This depression was Mother Archelon's nest in which to lay eggs. When she was young, there might be a dozen in number, but with the passing years she laid more and more until there might be two hundred in a nest! She arranged her eggs in layers, then covered them with sand. Now one more duty was to be performed she crawled back and forth and around and around, forming a maze of trails about the nest. These were not a great safeguard but they would serve to confuse other prowling reptiles in search of eggs.

Her mission accomplished, Mother Archelon lumbered back to the sea. The young, hatching sometime later, would also make their way to water—where many would be eaten by ammonites, fish or other reptiles. But some would survive to grow into monsters which, in turn, could devour the very enemies that had ended the lives of their baby brothers and sisters.

The first known ancestor of Archelon, and of all turtles, was discovered in Africa, where it lived more than two-hundred million years ago. It took about twenty-five million years after that (in Triassic times) for the true turtles to develop. From then on they flourished, spreading to all continents of the world as well as living in the seas. Unlike the dinosaurs, which became well established at about the same time, these awkward, lumbering reptiles survived to be part of our modern world. Sometimes they are called "living fossils."

Protosuchus, ancestor of the crocodile

Another hardy member of the "living fossils club" is the crocodile. Again the earliest known ancestor lived some two-hundred million years ago, when dinosaurs had become numerous but were not very large. The skeleton of this ancestral crocodile was discovered only a short time ago in Arizona. It was not big; the animal had been about the size of a large lizard. Its head was short, with a pointed nose and large eyes. Its limbs were much like that of modern crocodiles and it was protected by armor-like skin. Again a comparison may be made to the turtle, as we learn that 25 or 30 million years after the early ancestor an abundance of true crocodiles inhabited the earth. They varied considerably in size and in certain features, but all were long in form, all were meat eaters, all wore "armor," all were powerful and had dagger-like teeth with which to seize victims. All spent most of their time in water, but they chose different types of localities. Great numbers of them lived along streams and beside lakes on all the continents while others inhabited the seashore and even the open ocean. The record size for a fossil crocodile is fifty feet—perhaps slightly larger than some of the mighty sharks.

Had there been people in that long-ago reptilian world to navigate the seas, they would have sailed over an amazing variety of monsters. Fifty-foot reptiles and almost fifty-foot fish! Certainly the land, even with its great dinosaurs, could not lay claim to all the giants.

Chapter VIII

FOSSIL FORESTS AND FIRST FLOWERS

Before picking up again the story of animals on land, let us explore for a bit the fascinating world of prehistoric plants. When we last looked at it, the green world of the Carboniferous had had a severe set back from an ice age which came with Permian times. (This is not the Ice Age most generally mentioned in connection with the world's history. That came many millions of years later. The Permian glaciation was not world-wide, but was limited to the Southern Hemisphere.) Then, with the close of the Permian, plants as well as animals took a new lease on life.

Actually there are not a great many fossil plant remains from the beginning of the Triassic period, which followed the Permian. It is possible that in many regions of the world a very dry climate prevailed which produced neither abundant plants nor fossils. However, in the area which is now Arizona it happens that one of the most remarkable of all fossil treasures was made during Triassic times. We know it as the Petrified Forest. Pieces of fossil wood and tree trunks are scattered over hundreds of square miles, but in an area of about forty square miles are six actual fossil "forests." Once these were great pine and other stalwart coniferous trees that probably grew on the slopes which rose from the area where part of the Rocky Mountains now stand. An inland sea lapped against the base of the highlands, and when floods occurred many trees were broken loose by the force of the water and were carried along with it. Sooner or later they were deposited on some shoal where they became covered with mud and sand, and slowly, by chemical action, their wood fibers were infiltrated and replaced by mineral substances. The direct cause was doubtless alkaline waters, bearing silica in solution, which soaked into the logs. Small amounts of iron and manganese which color the silica are responsible for the bright hues seen today in the petrified trunks. The chemical transformation took place in such a way that, in many cases, every detail of the structure of the wood was preserved. Some of the wood is practically in the jewelry class—there are countless streaks of opal, chalcedony and agate—but for the most part the pieces are varicolored jasper.

Of the thousands of sight-seers who visit the Petrified Forest each year, many expect to find *standing* trees of stone and are disappointed to see the logs

Logs in Petrified Forest

lying on their sides, often broken into short lengths. An understanding of the "forest's" history, of course, would prevent any false hopes of finding standing trees. It is most unlikely that upright trunks would be subjected to the conditions necessary for fossilization. As the trunks lay in mud and sand, often the earth under them would be washed away by heavy rains or streams. Finally a wide gulch would be cut out, the walls of which could no longer support a heavy weight. So down would fall the stone trunk, breaking into pieces as it crashed to the floor of the gulch. There are, however, a number of sizable trunks—one especially that measures a hundred and eleven feet in length, which somehow escaped conditions that caused so many to crack up. Today, since it has been undermined, great stone piers have been placed underneath to give it support.

Not far from the Petrified Forest, in the mountains of New Mexico, is another good hunting spot for Triassic plants. One of the interesting discoveries there was a horsetail with stems four or five inches in diameter. On the same fossil bed were also fern leaves and leaves of the plants known as cycads. This was a type that was to become such an important part of the landscape during the Age of Reptiles that, like the dinosaur, it is a "trade mark" of those times. Later the cycads dwindled in importance, but today there are about seventy-five kinds still thriving. Most of these are found in the Southern Hemisphere. In the United States only Florida produces cycads. It has two kinds, both small, and the stem does not appear above the ground but sends up a crown of leaves with many sharp-pointed leaflets. Mexico has several cycads like this and also much larger types. One develops a trunk from three to six feet tall and leaves three or four feet long. Its large chestnut-like seeds are roasted or boiled and eaten, and the food known as sago is produced from its stems. There are other cycads in many parts of the world which also yield sago, and they are often called sago palms, although they are not at all related to true palms.

Returning from the present to the reptilian age, we find that many of the cycads were giants. One abundant form boasted leaves three or four feet long and from sixteen to twenty inches wide. These were actually made up of enormous broad leaflets that grew out from the sides of a woody leaf stalk, half an inch in diameter. They were almost square-cut at the tips, but at the base contracted to a point at which they were attached to the stalk. This form of cycad (known to science as Sphenozamites) grew abundantly in the area that is now Virginia and possibly was one of the important contributions to the great coal beds of that region.

Another abundant cycad, also found in the Virginia region, had equally enormous leaves, but the leaflets instead of being broad were very narrow— no more than half an inch wide. However, a great number of these narrow strips made up each leaf, and each was twelve inches long. They did not come to a point at the leaf stalk but were attached by their whole width.

A number of other types of cycads and cycad-like plants have been discovered in ancient Triassic rocks of Virginia, Sweden and certain other parts of the world; but for the most part they are not complete enough for satisfactory study. Moving forward to the Jurassic, scientists discovered an abundance of fossil remains which indicate that the flora of that period was quite similar in widely separated areas of the earth. This is easily understandable since the climate during Jurassic times was mild and comparatively uniform over a large part of the world. There was also a helpful situation in the practically continuous land areas that existed then. Even though there were great inland seas, such as one that extended from Alaska to Mexico and reached almost from our western coast to Colorado, the land had quite complete connecting links around the globe. Today many land areas of Jurassic times lie beneath open sea.

Despite the quantity and its world-wide distribution, the Jurassic flora does not appear to have had great variation. Outstanding were the ferns, conifers and cycads—now at the height of their glory. It is thought that at least two out of every five species were cycads. Horsetails, algae, lycopods and scale mosses were holding their own but apparently were not abundant.

Though conifers were an important part of the landscape, they were perhaps not so imposing as the early conifers, the cordaites, that existed in Carboniferous times. Certainly they were not to be compared in size. One of the most abundant and widely distributed is known almost entirely from its leafy shoots. Its branches were arranged on the stalk to form a flat spray; its thick leaves were wrapped around the branch and pressed closely to it. Some specimens have been found with cones attached but these were so poorly preserved that details could not be studied to any extent. This conifer, known as Brachyphyllum, in a general way suggests the modern cypress tree.

The ginkgo, one of our most adaptable decorative trees of today, may be traced back to Jurassic times. In fact it can possibly lay claim to being the "oldest" tree now living, in that it has come through the ages with so little change that any real difference in the leaves is almost impossible to find.

Jurassic landscape

You probably are familiar with its broad, flat, leathery leaves with forking veins similar to those on the common maidenhair fern. Because of this resemblance the ginkgo is often called "maidenhair tree." Today it is known as a cultivated tree rather than in a wild state, but it is extremely hardy and thrives along streets and pavements. Once it was considered a true conifer but now, principally because of the manner in which the seed is fertilized, it is put in a class of tree all by itself. Beautifully preserved fossil ginkgo leaves have been found by the hundreds in Jurassic rocks of Oregon, in many parts of Alaska, in England and in Siberia. The ginkgo rose in height above the generally low scrub-like trees of the Jurassic, and they with the ferns and typical cycads and conifers must have presented a pleasing picture of green vegetation.

The Cretaceous, the third and last major division of the age of Reptiles, was a time of change and dramatic development in the plant world. So much happened in this period that it seems unbelievable —until we stop to remember that it included sixty-five million years! Of great influence on plant life was the shift in land areas from time to time. In the early part of the Cretaceous the continents were comparatively low, and in many parts of the world there were wide extensions of sea over the land. Sea covered much of the interior portions of California and Oregon, but a high peninsula developed from Oregon to southern California. Later the sea spread over a broad belt from Cape Cod to Texas, and there was an enormous shallow sea, several hundred miles wide, connecting the Gulf of Mexico with the Arctic Ocean. This actually divided our continent into two parts: a large eastern section and a much smaller western area. By the close of Cretaceous time, however, this region was elevated again. The great western plains took shape and the Rocky Mountains began to uplift. At this time the sea was pushed back to just about the position it holds today.

It is easy to understand that during such tremendous changes in land and water areas there would be drastic changes in the kinds of life they supported. Furthermore we can realize that marine waters sweeping over land plants did not create conditions most favorable for preserving fossils. But in spite of all this, a large collection of early Cretaceous plant remains have been made. They show that, as in the Jurassic, the most important types were ferns, cycads and conifers. The conifers were apparently the largest and grew in imposing forests. At least five were kinds of sequoias, relatives of the magnificent giant sequoia we find growing in California today.

Then at last, after millions of years of green plants that had produced spores, and even seeds, without the benefit of flowers, an exciting development took place: the world was brightened by the appearance of flowering plants! Judging by the fossil record, a great group of them apparently sprang into ex-

99

istence quite suddenly; however, they must have had a long period of preparation before their changing nature was placed in a permanent record of stone.

It may seem strange that flowers would be considered big "news," since seed-producing plants had long been established. But there was a difference in the way the new type of plant, known as an angiosperm, managed its seeds. The seeds were produced in a closed seed box or ovary. (The Greek word *angio* means "box.") In other seed plants, such as conifers and cycads, the seeds do not have the benefit of a closed covering. The improved style of seed bearing brought new efficiency and eventually great beauty to the plant world. In a fairly short time after it was in operation, there had developed a number of shrubs and trees easily recognizable as ancestors of modern species. Among them the willow and elm families were represented, as were the water lily, laurel and grape families. Later in the Cretaceous period we find tremendously increased numbers of flowering trees and shrubs. There were magnolias, sassafras, bayberries, maples, eucalyptus (now found only in Australia), oaks and several kinds of large-leaved tulip trees.

The Far Northern territory that today is called Greenland was rich in sturdy vegetation, having a mixture of conifers and hardwoods. A most interesting discovery made there was the remains of a breadfruit tree. Today breadfruit is found only in regions close to the equator.

As the Age of Reptiles was drawing to a close there was a profusion of hardy plants living on the borders of the great inland seas that cut through North America. Most of them bore flowers, and apparently conditions for their growth were so favorable that they not only developed rapidly but split into different forms. Later many spread to far distant parts of the world.

With the angiosperms were included not only the plants that first come to mind when we think of "flowering" species—the dicotyledons or plants having two seed leaves in the embryo and stems which show a division into pith, wood and bark. Angiosperms also include the monocotyledons—the kind that have only one "first leaf" or cotyledon. Among the monocotyledons are the grasses, now so important a part of our landscape and food supplies.

Chapter IX

MAKE WAY FOR MAMMALS!

Not only were flowering plants in themselves an exciting addition to the earth, their development seems to have had an important connection with animal life. Fossil records show that when vegetation ceased to be limited to harsh, rough varieties having little food value, and began to include grasses with their nourishing seeds and other nutritious plants, there was an upswing in the fortunes of a kind of animal which had been of lesser importance. These were the mammals.

Mammals had entered the scene long before the coming of flowering plants, apparently having made a start very early in the Age of Reptiles. The name "mammal" is used as an identification because of the mammary (milk) glands by means of which a female gives nourishment to her young. This was an important characteristic that distinguished mammals from reptiles, which had no such way of nourishing their babies. There are other differences. Mammals are warm-blooded while reptiles are cold-blooded. This means that when temperatures fall very low a reptile's body temperature goes down too, until it cannot sustain life. If temperatures become too hot the reptile dies from too high a body temperature. The "warm" blood of mammals remains at nearly the same temperature no matter how the air surrounding these animals may vary. The mammals also have a body covering of hair or fur—a protection from the elements which no reptile enjoys.

Before the first true mammals appeared, there came into existence some odd kinds of creatures which are considered "mammal-like reptiles." In

Cynognathus, a mammal-like reptile

their habits they were true reptiles; but backbones, shoulder blades, hipbones, limbs and feet all showed characteristics of mammals. There was definite variety in the teeth of each of those in-between animals: some were designed for biting, some for tearing and some for chewing. In most reptiles the teeth are all more or less of the same pattern, and they are replaced throughout the life of the animal as fast as they are worn away or broken.

For something like forty million years the mammal-like reptiles flourished, during which time the first true mammals began their timid existence. Comparing them with mammals of today, it would be difficult to recognize them as such. Mostly they lived in trees or underbrush. Their food was largely seeds, fruits, insects and probably the eggs of small reptiles and birds. They laid eggs rather than producing living young; however, when the tiny, undeveloped young one emerged it was not left to fend for itself as a baby reptile would be.

After a time some mammals progressed beyond mere egg laying. They produced living offspring, but since these youngsters also were in an undeveloped state they had to rely completely on the mother for a while. Until they could be independent they lived in a pouch which covered her abdomen, where she supplied them with milk. Here another advance was shown from earlier mammals, for the milk came through a few nipples rather than simply oozing from the pores. These pouched animals were the first marsupials, a type of animal that is represented today by the opossum on our own continent and in Australia by the kangaroo and several other pouched mammals. Native of Australia, also, are two present-day holdovers from the still earlier mammalian form than the marsupials: the duck-billed platypus and the spiny anteater, or echidna. Though mammals, these odd creatures lay eggs.

As the Age of Reptiles gave way to the Age of Mammals, the egg-laying mammals were declining in importance, the marsupials were flourishing, and a third group known as placentals was evolving something new in reproduction. Placentals not only gave birth to living young, they produce well-developed babies that are not so dependent on the mother. The dominant animals of the earth today are placentals.

As we leave the Mesozoic era and enter a new one in which mammals gained supremacy, we have a fascinating question to think about: Why did the mighty dinosaurs disappear? Even though they became of less importance, why did not a few survive? And why did the fantastic flying pterosaurs and other reptiles that had made the earth their domain vanish completely?

No scientist will try to give in a few short sentences an explanation for the change in the earth's population between the Mesozoic and the Cenozoic eras. Too many complex matters are involved! But a very general kind of statement shedding light on the shift in importance from reptiles to mammals might be to this effect: at the end of the Mesozoic era (which was also the close of the Cretaceous period) the earth entered upon a new period of development. Not overnight, nor even over a few years, but very gradually mountains began to push up from flat swamps and plains and many tropical lowlands were replaced by cold, jagged mountain slopes. It was then the Rockies were born.

How easy it is to understand the hardships this would cause the mighty reptiles! Those that fed on abundant palms would find this tropical vegetation being replaced by hardwood forests. And if the plant eaters died away because of lack of food, the meat eaters could no longer prey upon them.

Besides the problem of food, the new temperatures must have brought hardship to the dinosaurs. Being cold-blooded, they must have been sluggish, and therefore unable to sustain the fast pace needed to hunt food under rugged conditions. The energetic mammals, on the other hand, may well have begun to prey upon dinosaur eggs in great enough numbers to have some effect on the reptilian population.

All these factors must surely have helped bring about the downfall of the dinosaurs. Yet the puzzle is not really solved, for why did every last dinosaur go? And why did not at least a few flying reptiles or the water-living plesiosaurs and mosasaurs survive as did certain crocodiles, turtles and lizards?

Scientists have wrestled with theories. One speculation is that an upset in the extinct animals' glands had a harmful effect. Another theory is concerned with the idea that creatures as a race can die out simply because they have lived their span and perish because of "racial old age." Still another possibility is that epidemics may have swept through groups of animals. There is no real evidence to support this thought, however.

Whatever the reason or reasons for the end of the dinosaurs, the dawn of the Cenozoic era (an era which brings us up to modern times) was sunset for the reptilian world. The reptile age had lasted about a hundred and forty million years. The Cenozoic which was being ushered in was to be comparatively short—no more than seventy million years' duration. But during this span of time the outlines of continents and seas as we know them today took shape, the great mountain ranges were altered to resemble closely the forms in which we know them today, and modern animal families became established. This is a good place, therefore, to look over the earth's geography. We can then follow with additional interest the fortunes of some of the more adventurous mammals.

The span of time between the latter half of the Mesozoic era and the first fifty million years of the Cenozoic was a period of ups and downs for land and sea areas. There is a possibility that a broad land mass had extended between Africa and South America. If it did actually exist, it was apparently about this time that the waters of the ocean we call Atlantic washed over that enormous area and joined with Antarctic waters. Another notable submergence is believed to have taken place where parts of southern Asia and northern Africa became covered with a body of water which we call the Indian Ocean.

In contrast to these "sinkings," there were some new land areas as the Cenozoic advanced. Central America, which had not been joined to the continent of South America, now stretched out, forming the Isthmus of Panama. Waters which had covered much of western Russia retreated, and what had been a tremendous sea sank into the confines of the Mediterranean as we know it today, with another waterway connecting the Mediterranean with the Black and Caspian seas.

Land was being formed in other ways also. One of these was volcanic activity, and we see some of the most spectacular results in the beautiful Hawaiian Islands. The volcanic peaks began to form some fifteen thousand feet under the water's surface—a great submerged chain of mountains. In time these built up until their summits rose over the waves and then continued to build until there was a large dryland elevation. Many of the Hawaiian volcanoes are still active but are well behaved, sending forth streams of molten lava from a side opening rather than in a destructive blast. Because the Hawaiian Islands have never been connected with other conti-

Volcano, builder and destroyer

nents by land over which animals could travel and plants could spread, they have a very special native "population." Before the first settlers arrived there from Samoa, the only inhabitants were snails, insects, birds and a few bats. Plants were limited to those which grew from spores and seeds carried by wind, ocean currents or birds.

A change in coast lines was not the only great alteration being made in the world's appearance as the Mesozoic era was drawing to a close. Ocean basins grew deeper and great seas were drained from the continents. On our own continent the Rocky Mountain area, which had been home to many dinosaurs, then was lost under a vast shallow sea, now reappeared. And as the earth continued to shift and fold, the great Rocky range was upraised. The Appalachians, which had first appeared in the eastern part of North America many millions of years earlier and had been quite worn away, were given an upthrust of several thousand feet. They, too, had a "new look." There was mountain building also in South America (the Andes), in Europe (the Alps) and in Asia (the Himalayas).

It is not surprising that with all the tremendous changes in land and water areas there should be changes in the world's climate. Ocean currents and winds were affected by both the changing outlines of the continents and the appearance of new mountain ranges. In turn these affected temperatures and rainfall, so there were many changes in local climate as the Cenozoic era progressed. Plants and animals died away in areas where moisture or warm temperature, to which they were accustomed, no longer existed.

But aside from changing local conditions there was a general world-wide trend in the climate. In the early part of the era it was generally warm and mild. As far north as London, England, tropical jungles flourished; and fig and magnolia trees grew in Alaska! But as the era wore on the balmy climes began to vanish. Pines retreated southward and much of the tropical vegetation was replaced by hardy oaks, vines and ginkgo trees. After some seventy million years of the Cenozoic, cold winds were blowing from newly formed polar icecaps and great ice sheets were beginning to creep over Europe, Asia and nearly half the continent of North America. This was the dawn of the great Ice Age.

Chapter X

TIMETABLE OF THE GLACIERS

Although we speak of "the" Ice Age as if it had been one continuous period, there were actually four separate periods of time during which glaciers dominated the earth; in between there was relief from the intense cold. This entire period lasted for a million years. These are the same million years that are known as the Pleistocene epoch on the geological time chart. It is interesting to note that each glacial period lasted only about fifty thousand years; the warm periods between the icy ones were far longer.

There were three main centers from which the ice sheets of the Northern Hemisphere originated. One center was in eastern Canada about Hudson Bay. A second was based in Scandinavia, while an Asiatic glacier crept forth from eastern Siberia. All were gigantic; the Canadian ice sheet alone was larger than the present Antarctic continent—close to five

Glacier

million square miles. Its thickness was eight thousand or more feet at the center, and its weight caused the whole of eastern Canada to sink several hundred feet!

What forces create such ice sheets? In one respect this question can be answered; in another it is an unsolved mystery.

The mystery concerns the underlying cause of cold spells so intense that enormous glaciers take form. A variety of theories have been suggested in explanation. Chief among them are: that the sun does not always give out the same amount of heat and its strength was reduced for a time; that a shift in the earth's axis threw the climate off balance. But these and other possibilities lack proof; they are theories and nothing more.

While the reason for the conditions that create glaciers are in doubt, their actual creation can be described with exactness. There are plenty of living glaciers still on earth to observe and study! A glacier starts high in the mountains where snow drifts into a hollow between peaks, or into a basin. If temperatures are low enough (as is the case above "snow line"), all of the piled-up snow does not melt. The year around, and year after year, some of it remains and fresh drifts are added. When the pressure of accumulated snow crystals is great enough, the lower layers are packed into solid ice.

An ice field cannot stand still. As with any other weight on earth, it is affected by the force of gravity. One result of this force is that the downward pressure tends to push outward the edges of the ice sheet. Tongues of ice are then forced outside the basin where it first took shape and through gaps between the mountain peaks. Also, as the glacier grows to reach a slope, gravity shoves it downward. Meanwhile more recently formed ice gathering on the heights supplies the glacier with additional area to the rear—and helps shove it along. The speed of glaciers has been clocked, and an average rate of seven and a half inches a day was revealed. This would result in an advance of about 225 feet a year.

Because of a glacier's tremendous force and weight, it is not halted by obstacles in its path. It either goes around such barriers as mountain peaks or carries lesser stumbling blocks along with it. There is one enemy that can put a glacier to rout: heat. When the ice reaches a climate mild enough to melt ice, the front or "snout" of the glacier begins to disappear. If the melting is faster than the supply of ice being pushed forward, the glacier begins to shrink or "retreat."

The last great ice invasion over the earth ended only about twenty thousand years ago. As a matter of fact in Greenland and the Antarctic an ice age still may be said to exist. On the geologic time chart twenty thousand years is such a short span that no one can say whether we today are merely in an inter-glacial period or whether an even climate will now prevail for millions of years as happened in the "good old days" of the dinosaurs.

During the great Ice Age, North America had a variety of glaciers. Not only was there the gigantic one that smothered Canada from coast to coast and pushed down into the United States, but many an ice sheet filled the valleys of our western mountains. These, however, did not join and become part of the vast continental glacier. It is interesting to realize that, bleak and forbidding as the glaciers were, it was the effect they had on the land that created much of our beautiful scenery. The Great Lakes, the Finger Lakes, the sparkling lakes of Wisconsin and Minnesota all are glacial products, for their basins were gouged out by the moving ice sheets. Countless waterfalls, including the great Niagara, had their origin in glacial action. Such marvels as the geysers of Yellowstone Park came into being because of it. In a more practical way also the great glacier created benefits that we enjoy today. It pushed over our central plains a deep covering of loam which is rich and fertile for crops.

But although we can appreciate these helpful and delightful results, the Ice Age must have held small comfort for the animals of that rugged time. Many plants and animals were forced southward—to Africa, southern Asia and the southern parts of America. Birds developed the habit of migration to meet the problem of having their usual feeding grounds covered with snow. Evidence uncovered by fossils reveals that many species of mammals disappeared completely during the Pleistocene. Mostly they were creatures of very large size. Perhaps the ice and cold were partly responsible for their passing; perhaps there were other causes. At any rate the Ice Age, or Ages, saw tremendous changes in animal and plant life, as well as in the earth's surface, within a comparatively short time.

As the animal populations of the different continents shifted their feeding grounds and hunted more friendly climates, two land bridges were of great

importance. One of these was the Isthmus of Panama, which joined North and South America. This connection between the Americas was maintained throughout the Ice Ages and remains to this day. The other extended outward from Alaska, connecting North America with Asia. This Alaskan land bridge was not always available. It would disappear from time to time beneath the cold waters of Bering Strait, even as it has in modern times. However, when it did furnish a footing for the restless and wandering creatures, it had a most important effect upon the distribution of the world's animal population.

Chapter XI

FAMOUS ANIMAL ANCESTORS

Having had a quick survey of the era that brought mammals from a position of minor importance to leading citizens of the world, let us now return to its early days. There we will find a number of strange and unimpressive little creatures, but if we follow their life stories and track down their descendants, we discover that they were the early ancestors of certain of our most popular animals of today. One of these is the horse.

Something like fifty million years ago in the territory that is now the state of Wyoming there was a certain mammal which science has christened Eohippus. Since "eo" is the Greek word for "dawn" and "hippus" for horse, you will know at once that Eohippus was the earliest ancestor of our fleet-footed racing champions and of faithful Dobbin, that helps many a farmer even in this age of machinery.

Fifty million years ago Eohippus showed no more signs of greatness than many of its neighbors. It was about the size of a fox, had an arched back, a short neck and legs that could scarcely be considered long. Perhaps its outstanding feature was its manner of walking, which was on the toes rather than on the soles of the feet. It had four toes on each forefoot and three on each hind foot. On these toes it could travel lightly over the forest floor. This was about the only indication that it had the makings of a swift runner.

Wyoming of long ago was not the only area in which the dawn horse lived. There were some of these animals in Europe too. But as ages passed the dawn horse of the Old World died away, so that there came a time when North America was the only continent that could boast of the horse as one of its citizens.

During this interlude the American dawn horse had given rise to a variety of descendants. One of these was the "midway" horse, known as Mesohippus. The midway horse was somewhat larger than the dawn horse, but still not so large as a timber wolf. It had three toes on each of its front feet (one less, you will notice, than Eohippus) and the middle toe was somewhat enlarged. A hoof was in the making.

More millions of years passed and more types of horses came into being. They had increased greatly in size, until they were about as large as our present-day ponies. The most important member of the horse family of this time has been given the name

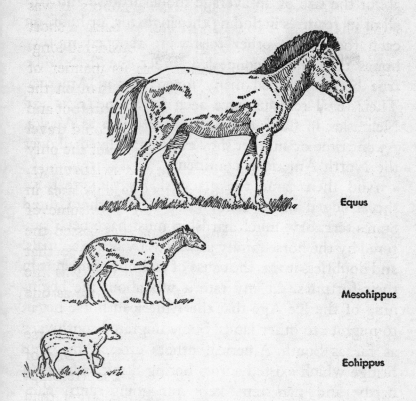

Horse

Equus

Mesohippus

Eohippus

Meryhippus. Like the others, it had three toes but, unlike them, used only the middle one to run on. As the era advanced, coming close to modern times, horses really began to show their possibilities. There were still a few holdovers of the three-toed species but there were also horses with single hoofs that strongly resembled the true horses that were to follow.

The first "true" horse is known as Equus. It was about the size of an average modern horse and had all of its features including the single toe, or hoof, on each foot. Two other toes were reduced to tiny bones completely concealed under the flesh. The true horses enjoyed many long years in America. Their fossil remains have been found in Texas and Nebraska, in California and as far north as Alaska. At one time or another they apparently lived all over the North American continent.

And then came the glaciers! As the great ice sheets edged down from Canada into the United States territory, much hardship must have been suffered by the horse family as well as by other animals, and doubtless it was the cause of an important shift in their fortunes. At any rate it was about the beginning of the Ice Age that the American horse began to migrate to other lands. Some migrated southward as far as South America; others crossed the land bridge which existed across Bering Strait. The most hardy and persistent kept on going until they reached Europe and even continued down into Africa.

Some of these adventurous travelers did not prosper in the new lands where they sought refuge. As ages went by they died out entirely in South America. In Africa zebras and asses (which may date back very far in the history of the horse family) survived, but no other horses. North America they had deserted. However in Europe, as the important new earth citizen known as "man" was establishing himself, Equus came into its own as an intelligent, swift and strong creature, eventually capable of being man's friend as well as helper.

At this time also another familiar animal roamed many parts of the world. It would seem familiar because it looked very much like an elephant, but close inspection would reveal differences. This prehistoric creature was the mastodon. The name "mastodon" has been given to a number of fossil elephants. They differed from true elephants in the structure of the skull, especially in the teeth. And some of the mastodons had tusks in the lower jaw as well as in the upper.

But the detective work of scientists takes us back ever further than the days when mastodons and mammoths roamed over Europe, Asia and North America—to about the time when Eohippus was establishing itself on earth. Discoveries and studies reveal that the very earliest known elephant ancestor lived in what is now the Libyan desert near Cairo, Egypt. It had none of the majestic bearing of later-day elephants, however. It was somewhat pig-like in form, but it had an unusually long upper lip and short tusks.

Time passed, and with its passing the descendants of this odd creature gradually became larger and heavier, and their bodies changed considerably in form. Legs lengthened, the head became large and the neck short. The massive head developed strong mus-

Mastodon

cles to support the heavy tusks that were increasing gradually in size. These new features might have proved a serious handicap, for the head was too far from the ground and the tusks too prominent for the owner to reach food on the ground. But a solution lay in a nose that lengthened into a trunk with

124

which the elephant can gather food and suck up water with scarcely a bend of its head.

There came a time when these early members of the elephant tribe began to look for new feeding grounds. Some of them crossed the great land bridge which then connected Africa and Europe. Some kept going to the east until they crossed the land bridge between Asia and Alaska, then continued southward over North America and even farther into South America. During its long history the elephant group had representatives living on every large continent of the world. One kind spread from Africa to Europe and to southern Asia, but never came to the American continent.

Various species of mastodons traveled more widely. Toward the end of the Ice Age they were distributed over the New World as well as the Old, and apparently were as much at home in cool swamps as in warm grasslands. One of the best fossil skeletons of a mastodon ever found was located in a dried-up lake bed near Newburgh, New York. From it, and other fossil discoveries, scientists picture the American mastodon as a large, bulky figure that stood some nine feet high at the shoulder, with a long body, thick legs and massive hips.

Mammoths were true elephants and were still mightier than the mastodons. Some stood fourteen feet high at the shoulder! Like the mastodons, they had strong, limber trunks and great ivory tusks, but there was considerable variety among them. Those that lived in North America have been divided into three main groups: the woolly mammoth, the Columbian mammoth and the imperial mammoth. The woolly seemed to thrive living near the borders of retreating glaciers; the imperial and Columbian mammoths preferred more temperate climates. The imperial mammoth, the greatest of all in size, ranged from Nebraska to Mexico.

Because the woolly mammoth lived close to the glaciers some extraordinary discoveries of its "remains" have been found. Not merely fossilized bones tell of this prehistoric creature's existence; complete bodies—flesh and skin as well as bones—have come to light. They were found in great blocks of ice in Siberia and Alaska where they had remained in a natural "quick-freeze" for many thousands of years. The bodies showed that the woolly mammoths wore warm coats of reddish fur mixed with long dark hair.

Human inhabitants came to North America long after they had been established in the Old World. As a result, on our continent, man did not have so long an association with mammoths as was the case in Europe. But in North America as well as in Europe, for many centuries man pitted his greater cunning and skill against the brute strength of these four-footed giants.

There is no clear evidence concerning the decline of the mastodons, but die away they did. Fortunately two types of mammoths survived in the form of the

African and Indian elephants that we know today.

Another history of growth, change and long migrations belongs to the camel family. This time, as with the horse, the beginnings of the family is traced to our own continent. It was many millions of years ago, early in the Cenozoic era, that a little creature no larger than a jack rabbit but identified as a "first" camel lived in North America. With the passing of some millions of years another, larger camel developed. This was about the size of a sheep.

More millions of years passed by, and as the earth grew older some animal families flourished while others lost ground. The camels, like the horse and elephant, were among the successful ones. By the Miocene epoch they were roaming over all the grassy plains of North America. A fascinating discovery was made in recent years of nearly a hundred fossil skeletons of Miocene camels, lying close together. It is believed that these animals may have grazed singly or in small groups during warm weather, but that as winter approached they banded together in great herds, After a night's rest a group would move on in the endless hunt for good grazing lands, but the old or sick members would be too weak to get up and would die where they lay. This could account for so large a number of skeletons being found in one spot.

The camels of Miocene days apparently resembled llamas more than they did the animals we call camels today. It is believed that they had no humps on their

127

Miocene camels

backs. Some were larger than the big modern two-humped camel of Asia, while others were smaller than the South American guanaco. One of them has been described as the "high" or "giraffe" camel, for it had the long slender neck and legs of a giraffe. Nevertheless, the form of its skull and feet place it in the camel family. During the same period there were living in western Nebraska camels whose necks and legs were not even as long in proportion to their bodies as is the case with our modern camels.

There is no doubt that camels prospered on our continent. The family was well represented in Oregon and Washington, in Nebraska, the Dakotas, Texas and Florida. But they, too, like the horses, mastodons and mammoths caught "migration fever." Certain groups traveled southward, over the Isthmus of Panama, until they reached South America. Others headed northward until they came to the land bridge between Alaska and Asia, and there crossed over to wander through Asia, Europe and on to Africa. In North America the camel family began to die away until a time came, as with the horse, when

"Giraffe" camel

not a survivor remained in the animal's original homeland.

In South America the family's representatives found conditions suited to their needs. Ages later, when people invaded that continent, they found among the native animals those members of the camel tribe known as guanacos. The llamas and alpacas, so valued in South America today, are believed to be domesticated forms of this beast. In spite of the facts that have been brought together about the earliest camels, little is known of the development of the one-humped Arabian camels or the two-humped Bactrian type. It is not even known for a certainty where, when or by what peoples camels were first domesticated.

As we think about the various animals that have migrated from continent to continent, it is worth considering how these migrations were carried out. Today when people migrate they usually know what destination they are headed for and why they are going. Naturally this is not the case with animals. Instinct, perhaps promoted by insufficient food supplies, causes them to wander. A group which starts out from home base travels intact only a certain distance; some are bound to fall by the wayside. But as some individuals die off they are replaced by young—and the march goes on. Eventually, perhaps after many generations, they come to a stopping place and a new homeland is adopted.

Chapter XII

PLANTS TRAVEL TOO

By now we have followed the history of many changes from the time life began on earth—changing climate, changing land and sea areas, and animals which altered in appearance and habits and which changed their homelands when living conditions became unfavorable. We have followed, also, a number of the great adjustments that occurred in the world's vegetation from the time plants first ventured out of water to live on land. But as we enter the Cenozoic era, in which climates and other conditions changed with ever increasing rapidity, we find the problem of survival becoming more acute. Rooted to the earth as they were, would plants be able to survive as their surroundings changed from hot to cold or from dry to wet, and back again?

It is true that countless different kinds of plants did weaken and die away, just as certain animals did, but great numbers that adorn our world today survived the Ice Age and other hard times as animals did: they adapted themselves to new conditions or they migrated, gradually pushing in the direction of favorable climes. The powers of adaptation are shown clearly by herbs. These are the plants that do not possess a woody stem above the ground, but are made up of softer tissues and usually die down to the soil after flowering. In some cases (the annuals) the entire life history is carried out in one year. In others (the biennials) the life history up to the ripening of the seed requires two years. A third type (the perennial) lives for several or many years and each season sends up from an underground woody stem a soft, non-woody stem that bears flowers and seeds. It is believed that the herbs are descended from woody plants.

Greenland, located in icy northern waters, gives us a good picture of changing plants in changing climates. Today this huge island, with an intensely cold climate, has few real trees. Some tiny willows have managed to survive the cold but they are less than a foot high and the "trunk" or stem, though it may show as many as fifty annual growth rings, is scarcely thicker than a pencil! Most of Greenland's plants are herbs of the perennial variety. They have a great advantage over other types, for they are able to complete a cycle of growth and mature their seeds in the short warm summer months, then survive the winter in the form of hardy seeds or by hibernating underground.

It was a different story in early Cenozoic times when Greenland was part of the North American continent. Then, if we could have walked over its low hills and the moist meadows of Greenland, we would have seen tall bald cypress trees, several kinds of cedars and sycamores, willows, elm, oaks, maples, tulip trees, sequoias and numerous other plants that flourish in our own country today. The study of thick beds of shale in Greenland has revealed the fossil remains or impressions of nearly three hundred various kinds of plants—and nearly all seem very different from those growing in that region today. The ancient vegetation would be at home in modern Maryland or Virginia; it is what we call a "temperate" flora. The present-day flora of Greenland is Arctic or sub-Arctic.

While trees and smaller plants were thriving in temperate Greenland, a number of the same species were growing in the southern United States. Actually there was a very rich flora in the area extending from North Carolina to Texas. More than six hundred different species have been recovered from the early part of the Cenozoic era—the period known as Eocene, when the "dawn horse" and the elephants' earliest ancestors were becoming established on earth. Some of these species were strange trees and shrubs which are now found mainly in Central America, the West Indies, various parts of the Old World and the northern part of South America.

Changing climate and local land conditions gradually altered the landscapes of various regions, and when we take a giant step from Eocene to Miocene times (over some sixteen million years) we find that many kinds of plants disappeared while strange new ones were coming into existence. Unfortunately fossil deposits revealing the flora of our country during this period are few. In all North America east of the Rocky Mountains there is only one deposit that is known to contain plants of the Miocene period. It is a small area in the District of Columbia and Virginia. Cone-scales, seeds and branchlets show that the bald cypress, so widespread during Eocene times, was abundant. There were also water elms, sycamores, sumacs and such shrubs as holly, huckleberry and bittersweet (all somewhat different from the species now living). On the whole the plant life was similar to that found today along the coast of South Carolina and Georgia and along part of the Gulf of Mexico.

Making up for the lack of exciting fossil discoveries in the eastern United States, from this particular period, there is a Miocene fossil deposit in the Rocky Mountains of Colorado which has been called "in many respects one of the most remarkable known anywhere in the world." In Miocene times a little lake was set high in the granite mountains, five thousand feet above sea level. It was no more than a mile wide and five miles long, and had been formed simply by the damming of a mountain valley. At its bottom was a thick deposit of papery shales which had been caused partly by volcanic ashes falling on the water's surface and then settling, and partly by mud and ashes being washed into the lake by rains, streams and waves. It was an ideal setting for fossil impressions to be made. Later much of the deposit was eroded and carried away, but in the remaining parts (from the Miocene) have been found thousands upon thousands of plant impressions, as well as more than thirty thousand insects and the remains of fishes, birds, and shells! This fossil treasure-trove that once was a body of water has been named Lake Florissant.

Lake Florissant shows the fossils of very many plants that adorn our country today. There were pines, junipers, poplars, ash, hickories, walnuts and an especially large number of oaks. And although the herb types of plants are always rare as fossils, some of these also are represented in the Lake Florissant deposits.

Besides the familiar plants that still flourish in the Rocky Mountain region as well as in other portions of the United States there are a number that are no longer native to our country but are found scattered in far distant parts of the world. One that has made an almost complete circle of the globe is the ailanthus, often called the "tree of heaven." In Miocene times it was native to Lake Florissant. Later it disappeared from there but was "native" in China and the East Indies. From these distant regions it was brought to eastern parts of the United States, where it became a favorite "naturalized" tree.

In general the fossil plants of Lake Florissant indicate that in Miocene times there was more moisture in that area than exists today, and it had a higher temperature. The climate possibly was like that of present-day North Carolina.

Another ancient lake bed in the far west gives a further picture of the plant life of our country before the great glacial invasions. In the vicinity of Spokane, Washington, lava once dammed up the river, forming a shallow lake several miles in length. Before the waters finally drained away hundreds of leaves, cones and other plant parts were preserved in the layers of clay and shales that had settled at the bottom. Many familiar tree families flourished there in Miocene times. Pine, cedar, willow, birch, oak, maple, cypress, magnolia and persimmon were prominent. Smaller plants were represented by cattails, pond weeds, grasses and tufted mosses. Enough fossil remains of the same trees and shrubs have been found in Oregon, Nevada and California to show that a similar plant life existed over much of the west during the Miocene.

Meanwhile wonderful forests clothed parts of central Europe. Covering Switzerland and nearby areas were dense woodlands made up of splendid palms, ferns, willows, walnuts, pines and many other trees as well as shrubs, flowering herbaceous plants, mosses and fungi. It was a vegetation similiar to the rich green growth found today in such tropical parts of the world as the Amazon Valley. Fortunately for

Dense forest of Switzerland

fossil hunters, beds of this flora were deposited in freshwater lakes, and the fine-grained material of which they are made up is excellent for preserving the delicate plant parts. It is estimated that central

137

Europe must have supported several thousand different species of plants in that long-ago day.

Then came the invasion of the glaciers, with lowering temperatures even where actual ice sheets did not exist. Some trees as well as smaller plants could not survive the change. Palms which had been so abundant in Europe are now represented on that continent by only one small species. Sequoias, now living only in our state of California, had several species in Miocene times in Switzerland. Certain of the European plants did escape, however, some moving eastward so that their descendants live today in eastern Asia. A few (especially those with small seeds) were able to pass over the mountains to take hold in southern Europe.

Though mountain masses were not absolute barriers to plant travel, they certainly were severe handicaps. The best avenues of escape were the lowlands. In the Old World there were two broad pathways used by plants. One was down through the lowlands of Asia by the valleys and coastal plains of China. Through this route seed migrants passed, and grew up among the "natives" of Asia. Many survived to the present day, giving China a wonderfully varied assortment of plants. A second route used by plants being pressed southward was down the Scandinavian peninsula into central and western Europe. There, however, many of them perished because they were blocked by the east-to-west mountain ranges.

On the North American continent the mountain ranges for the most part ran from north to south so that many plants were able to move southward through the valleys between. Not only American species but plants native to Asia used these routes. Apparently they crossed over the land bridge to the far north, then slowly pressed southward to the tropics.

It is surprising to notice that in some areas today vegetation thrives at the very edge of small glaciers. In Alaska ice sheets are bordered by splendid forests, as they come down to sea level; in the Alps wheat fields flourish with streams of ice pushing into their midst. Apparently these small glaciers do not affect their surroundings in the way a thousand-mile-wide glacier would. In any case we know that plants do not always have to retreat from difficult conditions. A number of remarkable adjustments have been made to their environment. The cactus is possibly the best known, with elaborate devices for holding onto the precious bit of water that falls in a desert. Certain other plants growing where there is an oversupply of rain have special openings known as water pores, usually located at the tips of leaves, through which excess moisture may escape. Sometimes a reduced number of breathing pores in the leaves helps control evaporation of water; and even the seeds and capsules of numerous plants may be regulated to suit special conditions. For instance in wet country the capsules open only in dry weather, staying closed to protect the seeds from abundant rains. In arid regions capsules remain closed during dry periods, opening only when moisture can refresh the seeds.

The habits of plants living today, as well as their distribution, offer many clues to the changes that took place in the plant world in prehistoric times. And fossil remains help us to understand how, where and sometimes why these changes occurred.

Chapter XIII

ALL WERE GIANTS

The biggest of creatures are not always the most successful but, because of their size, at first glance they hold a special interest. In the prehistoric story we have already come across a number of giants such as the largest of the dinosaurs, the sharks, the whales and the mammoths— but there were a number of other monsters that roamed the ancient plains and woodlands. Choosing a few of the most outstanding, let us meet them as a group based on size rather than the age in which they lived or on their localities.

Leading our parade is the titanothere, a word that actually means "giant beast." There were a number of different species but each of them resembled an overgrown rhinoceros—an animal with which they have a close relationship. On our own western prairies was one of the smaller titanotheres, but even he grew to a length of a dozen feet and

141

was perhaps six feet tall, with tremendous bulk. A larger species, the "battering-ram" titanothere, roamed the plains of Asia, and still others were at home in eastern Europe. One way in which "titan" differed from a rhinoceros was in tooth structure. And while the titanothere apparently had horns similar to a rhino's, the horns of the prehistoric beast were actually bony growths from the skull which projected across the nose. In contrast, a

Titanothere

Woolly rhineroceros

rhinoceros horn is made up of countless hairy fibers jointed together in a hard pointed mass which is attached to the nose. On a two-horned rhino, the horns are set one in front of the other, whereas the titanothere with two horns had them growing side by side.

Titanotheres were at the height of their glory about thirty-five million years ago. The day of the dinosaur was long since over and the earliest horse ancestors had given way to the larger three-toed kind. Big though the titan was, and ferocious in appearance, he was not a menace to his fellow creatures, for he ate leaves rather than flesh. He was doubtless awkward in his movements and used his

Baluchitherium

power and strength mainly against any daring carnivorous raider that tried to steal a calf from his herd. The titanotheres of North America spent their days browsing in vegetation, wading in streams and resting on the prairies that covered much of the land we know as South Dakota, which then was low and moist.

A still greater monster was Baluchitherium, which lived in Asia some fifteen or twenty million years ago. Actually he was a rhinoceros. But what a giant rhino! Standing eighteen feet high at the shoulders and measuring at least twenty-five feet from nose to tail, he was the largest land mammal of all time. He was given his name because the first fossil bones of this giant were discovered in the Asiatic country of Baluchistan. Like the titanotheres, Baluchitherium had hoofs but, unlike them, he wore no horns.

By the time of the Pleistocene Ice Age, South America had its own share of big beasts. Outstanding was the ground sloth, a huge shaggy-haired beast from eighteen to twenty feet long. Its oversized head was in good proportion to its heavy body; its legs also were heavy, and it walked awkwardly on the outer edges of its feet. Long powerful claws gave it a frightening appearance but it had no need to use them as offensive weapons against other animals, for it was a plant eater. To secure leaves it apparently sat on its hind legs and, thus raised to an upright position, grasped tree branches in the claws of its front feet and pulled them downward. Its extraordinary, long tongue then curled around the leaves and drew them into its mouth. Fossils indicate that the giant ground sloths survived until fairly recent times—at least recent enough to have shared the pampas with humans.

Big as they were, the ground sloths suffered many casualties from such enemies as the saber-toothed tigers. These great cats were as large as lions and had remarkably thick, strong forelegs and necks. They had vicious claws, too, but their prize weapons were the two dagger-shaped canine teeth, almost eight inches long, that protruded from the upper jaw. With these, victims could be stabbed to death.

Neighbors of the giant sloths of South America were giant armadillos known as glyptodons. They somewhat resembled enormous turtles, having a shell five or six feet long. This was made of small bones fastened together. Bony rings also covered part of the tail, which ended in a heavy spiked club—a fan-

Glyptodons

tastic creation which resembled the tail of the dino-saur, Ankylosaurus. Unlike the modern armadillo, which can roll itself into a ball when attacked, the glyptodon's solid shell of bony plates made such a retreat impossible. Possibly when such a frighten-ing enemy as a saber-toothed tiger came near, the glyptodon simply crouched close to the ground, tucking his head close to the shell. Some of these bulky animals (though not the type with the spiked tail) traveled northward across the Isthmus of Pan-ama to the North American continent.

Another big fellow that was strictly South Amer-ican was the toxodon. About the size of a rhinoceros but with a body more like a hippopotamus, he spent much of his time swimming or wading in swampy lakes and rivers.

As far north as the state of New Jersey in Pleisto-cene times were some different "giants." There was the moose-like deer named Cervalces (a combina-tion of *cervus* and *alces*, "deer" and "moose"). This bulky deer had horns unlike those of any re-cent species, and its habits were undoubtedly similar to those of a moose. Among his neighbors was the giant beaver—perhaps not so enormous as other of the prehistoric "giants" but huge compared with the beaver living today.

Across the Atlantic in the British Isles and other European countries was another magnificent mem-ber of the deer tribe. He is known as the Irish elk, for skeletons—some practically perfect, even to the great spreading antlers—have been found frequently in the bogs of Ireland. The head of this handsome animal seems surprisingly small for his large body, which was broad and some six feet high at the shoulder. However, his neck was powerfully built, enabling him to hold aloft his spreading antlers, which might measure as much as ten feet from tip to tip. This is very much larger than those carried by any modern deer. His weight doubtless caused many an Irish elk to lose his life in the bogs where, having sunk into the ooze, he could not pull himself free again. These great mammals survived until recent times, becoming extinct less than a thousand years ago.

Giants of the bear world lived during the Pleistocene times in France and Spain. Commonly they are called the "cave bears" of Europe, for, with early man, they made use of the protecting caves in the Pyrenees Mountains. They were massive brutes, though actually not so large or tall as the mighty Kodiak bears that live in Alaska today. A prehistoric cave bear was about the size of a very large grizzly but its head was much larger in proportion to the size of the animal, and the legs were short and massive. They must have been fearsome monsters for the cave men to deal with; nevertheless, they were apparently neither so ferocious nor so speedy as the lions, wolves and many of the other beasts that roamed the ancient hills and forests.

Today we look with respect at the remaining

bison that are survivors of the mighty herds once hunted by American Indians. They are the modern giants native to our continent. But fossil hunters have discovered from time to time the remains of prehistoric bison of much larger size than their modern relatives. They wore enormously long, mas-

Irish elk

sive horns, some six feet across at the tips, and the body was bulkier in every respect than the bison of today.

On the other side of the world, Australia was supporting its own type of giants. The land that once joined this area to southeastern Asia had long since disappeared beneath the sea, leaving an island continent on which animal life followed an independent course of development. Instead of giving rise to placentals (the highest class of mammals), this region was promoting the development of marsupials and egg-laying mammals. A number of these flourish today, prominent among the marsupials being the kangaroo. Some of these are large, fully six feet in height when standing erect on the hind limbs. This size was far surpassed by certain fossil species, however. One extinct kangaroo had a head almost as large at that of a horse, and a possible height of ten or more feet. What a picture this enormous beast must have presented, bounding across the fields as if with a pogo stick, on its powerful hind limbs! Another marsupial known as the wombat today is no taller than two feet at the shoulder, but late in the Age of Mammals the wombat relative was a really large, bear-like creature.

Mammals were not the only kinds of animals that had their giants; some thirty million years ago huge flightless birds were native to practically every region of the earth. In the area that is now Wyoming lived Diatryma. This huge feathered creature had

Diatryma

long powerful legs but tiny useless wings, or possibly no wings whatever. It was seven feet tall, with a head as large as that of a modern horse. In Diatryma's time the small three-toed horses were probably eaten by these great birds.

During the Pleistocene, millions of years later, another kind of bird, the moa, was flourishing in New Zealand. There were many different types, the biggest of them being ten or more feet in height. These giants became extinct long before people discovered New Zealand, but some of the smaller types survived until about that time. The moa's only means of defense was a powerful kick with its stocky legs and heavily clawed feet, and it had no wings with which to fly from danger. Another bird, which lived on the island of Madagascar, was not quite so large as the moa (it was a mere eight feet tall) but it laid the largest bird eggs ever seen. They were about nine inches by thirteen, and held more than

151

two gallons of liquid. It is thought that the remains of some of these giant eggs inspired the story in the Arabian Nights of the "roc"—a bird of "monstrous" size with legs "as big as the trunk of a tree."

Today the ostrich represents the giant of the bird world and there are a number of giant mammals, including the elephant and the whale. Surveys reveal, however, that during the Ice Age there was a decided falling off of mammals in the world's population and that a number of the creatures that vanished were of large size. Many important groups of mammals had at least one giant form during the Pleistocene which did not survive into modern times. But while certain mammals were falling by the wayside a new citizen of the earth was preparing for the dawn of a new era—the Age of Man.

Chapter XIV

THE GROWTH OF A FAMILY

Now that we have come to the dramatic part of the earth story where human beings take a leading role in developments, we may think back to the Indian arrowhead mentioned at the beginning of this book. Yes, arrowheads have helped scientists to picture events that occurred before history was recorded. And countless other remains of the "earliest Americans" have been found scattered over, and buried in, the plains and hills of North America. It might seem that checking up on the activities of prehistoric people was fairly simple. However, the "simplicity" vanishes when we realize that man appeared on our continent only after hundreds of thousands of years of human progress.

Where shall we look for his beginnings?

A hundred years ago this would have been a completely baffling question. A start had been made in understanding the nature of fossils, but all the

153

prehistoric discoveries were concerned with the lower forms of animal life. As a matter of fact, when the first bits of evidence on the nature of early man were found and presented to the public, almost no one wanted to believe in them. Even scientists rejected the idea of people having lived before they had the ability to make and work with tools. Modern man preferred the idea that humans had always had a degree of what we call "civilization." However, as more and more evidence of human growth was gradually brought together, he began to feel that this development was even more miraculous than his former theories. Scientists and public alike at last were able to think about the subject with open minds.

Fossils have played a most important part in working out the story of prehistoric man; nevertheless, they are rare as compared to fossilized bones of other kinds of life. Enough have been found to reveal the differences in anatomy of the various human races as they existed hundreds of thousands of years ago, but without other clues the most skilled scientist could reconstruct very little of the ancient scene. One important source of knowledge is the tools and weapons made by prehistoric people, and in time various forms of art were created and survived to help picture their life and interests.

According to the evidence of fossils, the very first branch of the human "family tree" existed in Africa, but it was in Asia that the first known ancestors of modern man developed. This type is generally called Pithecanthropus erectus. The much-discussed Neanderthal was a considerably later type whose homeland was Europe. Homo sapiens, coming still later, is the type to which the modern races of mankind belong. These developments—from most primitive types to modern man—are believed to have taken place within something like the past million years. This, of course, places them within the framework of the Pleistocene period. However, in reference to man's culture rather than to geology, the same span of time has another name. It is called the Paleolithic or Old Stone Age. A "New" Stone Age was to follow before the Age of Metals brought drastic changes to man's way of life. Pithecanthropus lived during, and possibly before, the second interglacial period. The Neanderthal are known in Europe from the period between the third and fourth great glacial invasions. A later group of European residents have been named Cro-Magnon. As we shall see, these two later types were named for the places where important discoveries concerning them were found. Pithecanthropus erectus may be translated as "erect ape-man."

Discoveries revealing man's history were not made in an order that corresponded with their age. The first important find that was recognized as belonging to prehistoric man was made in 1828 and it happened to be in Europe. It was a weapon used by the Neanderthal. More than fifty years passed before the first remains of Pithecanthropus came to light; but let us follow this story first, since Pithecanthropus existed earlier than the Neanderthal.

In 1887 a young Dutchman named Eugene Dubois, still a college student but very greatly interested in the history of mankind, decided that the Far East would be a likely place to uncover early human fossils. He had read that great beds of animal bones had been found on the island of Java, off the coast of India, and felt that among them might be human remains. Since he could not interest anyone in financing an expedition to hunt for them, he joined the army as a surgeon in the Dutch East Indies, where he spent all his off-duty hours searching for fossils. After two years of this part-time work the Dutch government asked him to undertake "bone hunting" as a full-time job. Now all his waking hours could be devoted to the search. A rich treasure was discovered at a steep riverbank where bones were sticking out of the standstone, in plain sight.

Mr. Dubois began to dig and he continued digging for many months until he was at the level of the stream. And at last he found the prize—a tooth that had a distinctly human crown! A short time later he came across a skull that was too large to have belonged to an ape; he suspected it must be the remains of a very ancient and primitive man. He continued his search and finally, a short distance from the skull discovery, a long, straight thighbone came to light. The three parts—tooth, skull and leg bone—convinced him: he had found proof of an early man who had walked in an upright position. Pithecanthropus erectus would be a suitable name for him.

But although Mr. Dubois felt so sure of the importance of his discovery, he found no one would share his enthusiasm. In fact his belief was opposed so strongly that he finally began to be afraid he had been mistaken. Then about seven years later new evidence was added to his own. A mining adviser to the Chinese government, J. Gunnar Anderson, enjoyed the hobby of bone collecting. Several tremendous hunting grounds came to his attention, the greatest of all in interest being a wall of limestone not far from the city of Peking. As he climbed about it he discovered a huge cave. In it were a number of animal bones that seemed a strange assortment to be found together—and in a cave. There were remains of rhinos, bears, and even the jaws of a pig.

Of course all these bones could have been brought into the shelter by flesh-eating beasts, but a different discovery suddenly threw new light on the puzzle. There were chips of quartz; and quartz was not a natural part of this sandstone cave! Could they have been brought there and used by someone with real fingers? Because of difficulty in getting help with his digging, two years passed before he was sure of his answer. The "answer" was in the form of two teeth. They were human teeth. Before long

Chips of quartz—an important discovery

many more such teeth, parts of human skulls and a brain case were found. Mr. Anderson felt he surely had come upon a very early ancestor of the human race, one that lived about the time of Pithecanthropus. Since that time a number of other discoveries in the area have added to his evidence and scientists have identified bones as belonging to about forty adults and children who lived there between a quarter and half a million years ago. These people were identified so closely with Pithecanthropus

Peking man's tools for cutting and scraping

erectus (who had existed only a little earlier) that they were given the name Pithecanthropus pekinensis.

The size of his brain indicates that Peking man had the ability to think beyond the powers of all other creatures of his time. And evidence bearing out this idea was furnished by the quartz implements found in his caves: they showed he had been a toolmaker. Also remains of hearths with charred bones of animals nearby revealed that he had discovered the art of making fire and had the skill to use it for cooking. But he still had not found a way to kill animals (the quartz was used only for cutting flesh); he had to steal meat from the flesh-eating mammals. It is evident that he used a cave as "home," but it is not known whether he fashioned any kind of covering for his body.

Leaving this early ancestor of mankind in the Far East, we embark on another voyage of discovery with someone who was no scientist but who had an inquiring mind and keen imagination. He was a Frenchman named Jacques Boucher de Perthes. Although a collector of taxes, his interest in ancient man was far more keen than his interest in money, and he spent endless hours searching in gravel pits near his home in Abbeville, hoping to find some relic of early humans. At last (the year was 1828) he came across "evidence." It was a six-inch piece of flint from which two chips had been struck to give it a cutting edge. Mr. Boucher de Perthes was sure this bit of flint, and two similar ones that followed, had opened doorways to a vast store of knowledge. However (as happened with Mr. Dubois some years later), scientists were not impressed. Mr. Boucher de Perthes had to work on alone. Even when he found an actual stone hatchet the doubters overruled him. "Not so old as you think it is," was their verdict.

For years this remarkable man continued his search for flints that bore the evidence of use by primitive people. His only aid was from laborers whom he paid to dig in the gravel. He had been hunting for nearly ten years before the first three sharpened flints and the hatchet were found, but in the following nine years such quantities turned up that he established a home museum in which to display them. Carefully he placed them in order— from crudely shaped pieces of flint to well-constructed hatchets, knives and hammers. There were even large weapons in the form of javelins.

But scarcely anyone came to see his museum. Mr. Boucher de Perthes wrote a book describing his prized exhibits. Those who read it called his ideas fantastic. Finally, however, a break came in the total disbelief. A Dr. Rigollot was persuaded to visit the museum. He left it completely convinced that there had been a "Stone Age man."

Having found an ally and fellow believer in the evidence of the flints, Mr. Boucher de Perthes renewed his efforts to convince others—and confidently predicted that someday skeletons of the people who had fashioned the tools and weapons would be found. They were. It was the first time the modern world became acquainted with Neanderthal man!

The historic discovery that began a solid acquaintance with the Neanderthal was made in Germany in the Neander Valley near Dusseldorf. The year was 1856, when workmen were quarrying limestone there and came upon a little cave. In it were some bones—of no especial interest to them—but in the evening they did mention to friends what they had seen. Fortunately the news soon reached the owner of the quarry, and without delay he had the bones brought to him.

Thus, casually, a skullcap and thirteen other parts of a historic skeleton were rescued. They were examined by a scientist who pronounced them "human" and "very, very old." By this time an English scientist, Hugh Falconer, had made a trip to the Boucher de Perthes museum. He was amazed at what he saw, and he could not help but feel there was a connection between the flints and the skeleton from the Neander Valley. Quite likely this was one of the men who had made stone tools and lived in the days of long-extinct mammals. If only a human skeleton, such as the Neanderthal, could be found in very close association with bones of the extinct mammals!

There was to be no quick success in the quest

however. For thirty years no helpful discovery was made; then in Belgium one came to light. A small cave on the estate of a nobleman had attracted some attention because pieces of flint and bones of extinct animals were uncovered there from time to time. At last two Belgian scientists started to explore, not the cave itself but a terrace many feet high that stretched out in front of the cave. As they dug down through one hardened layer after the other, a great variety of "remains" were revealed: bone arrowheads, bits of pottery, flints, charcoal, and all manner of animal bones. But in the fifth layer lay the real prize—two human skeletons! And the heavy skull, low sloping forehead and projecting ridge of bone across the brow over the eye sockets proclaimed them to be the same type of man as that discovered in the Neander Valley. Since that time many more complete finds have been made in various regions, but especially in caves and rock shelters of France. However, the word "Neanderthal," dating back to the first startling revelation in Germany, continued as the official name for these early Europeans.

Actually the name "Neanderthal" is now used in reference to nearly a dozen related races who lived in Europe, Africa and the Far East. And sometimes people speak of the Neanderthal when they have in mind primitive people of a mere sixty or seventy thousand years ago. However, let us look at the "typical" Neanderthal man. He lived in

Europe (probably having had an Asiatic background) and was established there for something like a hundred thousand years before our own race, Homo sapiens, appeared.

The Neanderthalers were short in stature: the men averaged slightly more than five feet in height, the women less than that. Because they lacked a bend in the neck, such as enables us to hold our heads in upright position, and their thighbones were curved forward, their posture must have been most ungainly. The large broad head with sloping forehead, massive ridge across the eyes and almost complete lack of chin surely made him an unattractive specimen according to our modern standards of beauty.

As with the beasts and birds of prehistoric times, fossil bones give a picture of the physical appearance of Neanderthal man. But to add to this knowledge we have also the record of his stone work, for in spite of his primitive appearance the Neanderthal was a thinking creature who created weapons and tools.

When he first moved into Europe making a living was simple enough, for the time was during an interglacial period (between the third and fourth great glaciers). The climate was balmy, and deer, antelope and other game were plentiful. He had learned to make fire by causing sparks to fly from pieces of flint into wood dust or dry moss, and he had begun to use fire to cook meat. Because of the warmth he needed no shelter other than a windbreak made of bushes or an animal skin fastened between two trees.

Thousands of such easy years passed for the Neanderthal people, then little by little changes were felt. Winters were longer, colder, damper. Snowdrifts turned to ice instead of melting. Woolly mammoth and woolly rhinoceros replaced herds of tropical game. Neanderthal man had two choices: he could leave the land of his forefathers and migrate southward, hoping for better conditions, or he could stay and fight the cold. He chose the latter. Now he used fire for warmth as well as for cooking. Now he learned to use animal skins as clothing instead of a mere windbreak. Now he looked to caves and rock shelters for protection, and he had to improve on his weapons to kill the mighty, heavily coated beasts from the north.

In looking for caves, he found a real "housing" problem. There was not an abundant supply of them, and nearly always they were occupied by great bears and fierce lions. Here again fire came to his aid. He learned to build a blaze at the entrance of a cave, allowing the smoke to drift through the entrance. Before long any animals inside would be driven out, confused and frightened by smoke and flames. The shelter now was taken over by the inventive Neanderthal—who by this time could accurately be called a "cave man."

A really good cave for homemaking was one that was large and roomy and had a natural opening in the roof through which smoke could escape. In such a retreat a whole group might combine their living efforts. The women scraped and prepared pelts for clothing, roasted meat, tended the fire and stored up firewood. The men's work mostly concerned hunting. They had learned to drive bison, wild horses and giant deer over cliffs and to trap the woolly mammoth in pits: killing helpless animals with a stone knife or hatchet was not difficult. The hunters would skin and cut up their prey where the kill had been made, bringing back to the cave only the useful parts. After feasting on the returns of a hunt, unused meat was dried and stored away. Altogether the mode of life of the Neanderthal people begins to take on a familiar pattern of family-circle "breadwinning" and saving for future needs. Apparently, too, the Neanderthaler developed a feeling of reverence for life, to which he gave expression by sometimes, at least, affording a proper burial to those who died. A number of examples of carefully made graves have been found which definitely are as old as the Neanderthalers.

But despite all his advances, Neanderthal man had not found the key to survival. By the height of the fourth glacial period he seems to have vanished quite completely. No doubt one reason for his extinction was the cruel hardship brought on by the advancing glaciers. Then there was another. As the glaciers began to retreat the Neanderthal was faced with an enemy in the form of a new race of men.

They came from the East and had at their disposal an even keener knowledge of making and using weapons and tools than that of these earlier men of Europe. Quickly they took over the good caves, the best hunting grounds; and so perished the last of Neanderthal man. The newcomers are the first to be known as Homo sapiens—a name that means "wise men." They are the same species as ourselves and may be considered our true ancestors.

Chapter XV

REAL MAN AND REINDEER

Today reindeer usually come into our thoughts only as a part of Christmas legends, but to Laplanders and to many Eskimos they are a necessary part of existence. These people of the Far North can well understand the debt that Homo sapiens owes to this unique deer. When the "wise men" were establishing themselves in Europe, great herds of reindeer roamed the plains. Not only did they furnish plentiful food, but their skin was used for shelters and clothing and their antlers were fashioned into countless weapons and tools. So important were they to the existence of the first true men that the closing years of the Old Stone Age are often referred to as the Reindeer Age.

The race of Homo sapiens, even in those early days, was not limited to just one type of person. There were several varying groups that came from Asia to adopt Europe as their homeland; but the most successful and interesting of the invaders were the Cro-Magnon. There were very distinct differences in the physical appearance of these people and the Neanderthal. The Cro-Magnon was tall, the men averaging slightly over six feet. They had high foreheads, well-developed noses and chins, and they were able to carry their heads erect. No doubt about it: the Cro-Magnon was handsome indeed compared to those who had gone before!

At first the Cro-Magnon were as dependent on caves as the Neanderthal had been, but as the glaciers moved away and they began to enjoy a milder climate they often used tents, and dwelt in large open-air encampments. Like the Neanderthal, they were dependent on hunting for their food supply, and as years went by they became increasingly skillful and inventive in creating tools and weapons. Carefully made spearheads of flint or bone were fastened to the ends of wooden shafts with leather thongs. Now they could spear animals of large size. A harpoon was fashioned by carving a reindeer antler into a barbed dart and attaching it to a long leather thong with a stick tied to the other end. When such a harpoon was thrown forcibly at an animal the dart pierced the flesh and held there. The thong trailed behind and the stick became tangled in vegetation, pinning down the wounded beast. Besides these hunting aids the Cro-Magnon later made bows and arrows.

Even beyond these inventions there was a most

important development in Cro-Magnon times. The value of "secondary" stone tools was discovered. These were made purely for the purpose of creating better tools of bone and wood to use in actual manufacturing. For instance, a man took the trouble to construct an efficient scraper to shave down the shafts of spears or darts. He made an awl for drilling holes

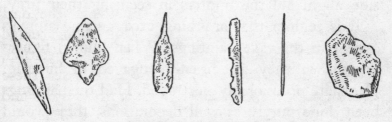

Prehistoric "tool kit":
Weapon points, Awl, Saw, Needle, Burin

in implements of bone or wood, as well as a variety of chisels. Antlers, bones and mammoth ivory might now be turned into polished pins, awls and beautifully fashioned spearheads. A man with a "tool kit" begins to seem civilized indeed.

Beside his ability in practical matters, the Cro-Magnon man had another side to his nature. He was artistic. There came a time when his desire for brighter and more cheerful surroundings inspired him to invent a stone lamp, operated with animal fat. Then as the walls of his dark caves were illuminated for the first time he was further inspired—to draw on them pictures of the animals he hunted. It is believed that these animal pictures had more meaning than mere decoration; they were probably concerned with hunting magic. Even today primitive hunting tribes believe that if they portray animals in this fashion they are given a certain influence and power over them. Thus portraying a large herd of bison and many horses and mammoths should result in these animals producing young in great abundance. Or a picture of a game animal with a spear thrust into its side might aid the hunters in securing their prey.

It is seldom that anything except game animals appear in the cave paintings. When human figures are shown they are usually engaged in hunting; plants are occasionally portrayed. Had the paintings been done purely as wall decorations, they would undoubtedly have been toward the front of a cave,

170

in the "living" quarters. Instead they usually are found far back in the dark recesses.

In the early art attempts the pictures were done in black, and were flat outlines showing only one hind leg and one front leg for an animal. But, with time, the cave artists began to use vivid, beautiful color and produced some work that critical viewers of today call "masterpieces." They made their paints by grinding lumps of red and yellow ocher and other dark earths with tallow. Also the artists engraved their pictures on some walls and sculptured others. A later phase of their art was sculpturing and engraving objects of bone, antler or ivory. Often handles of their tools or the ends of spear throwers

Cro-Magnon artist

were fashioned expertly into the form of bird or mammal.

Besides a number of inventions and developments of their own, the Cro-Magnon borrowed some ideas from neighboring people. Not far from them was another group who were also great hunters, their special prey being the fleet-footed wild horses that grazed and galloped over the plains. One use they made of their victims was to fashion tools of horse bone. A wonderfully helpful invention was none other than the needle. It was started with a sharp, narrow bone splinter smoothed and shaped into an awl. Then into the wider end a hole was drilled through which a dried tendon was pulled. Now the sharply pointed end could pierce through pieces of animal hide, and the sleek little awl would pull the tendon along after it. By this simple device skins could be sewed together, and all sorts of possibilities opened up in clothing and tent making.

You will remember that the early clues concerning the nature and location of both the Neanderthal people and Pithecanthropus erectus were discovered because of thoughtful investigations by brilliant men. The first knowledge of the Reindeer men resulted from a farmer's going on a rabbit hunt in southern France. When the pursued rabbit slipped into a large hole the impatient hunter thrust his hand in, hoping to pull out the little animal. Instead his hand closed over part of a human skeleton. Startled, he dug at the opening in the hill and soon found it to be the clogged-up entrance to a cave. The cave was nearly filled with human bones!

This was in 1852, some years after Mr. Boucher de Perthes had started his remarkable work on flints, but a few years before the skeleton was found in the Neander Valley. Very likely the farmer had never heard of Mr. Boucher de Perthes or his ideas about prehistoric man. It is easy to picture his amazement at the storehouse of skeletons to which the rabbit had led him with no thoughts of the distant past to enlighten him. He rushed to the mayor of the village of Aurignac to report a possible crime. The mayor was not troubled by a vivid imagination; he simply saw a duty to be performed. Without delay seventeen skeletons of men, women and children were removed from the cave and given a "decent burial."

The story might have ended there, but fortunately it had caused enough excitement for the villagers to tell friends and relatives about it. Slowly the news traveled about France, and eight long years after the discovery a lawyer, Edouard Lartet, decided to investigate. He was a friend of Mr. Boucher de Perthes and was also deeply interested in the beginnings of man. By this time the Neanderthal find had been made but it was still not taken seriously by more than a handful of people.

Mr. Lartet's disappointment was keen when he asked the mayor of Aurignac if he might see the skeletons and discovered they lay in a local graveyard. He would not be allowed to go digging there! How-

173

ever, he set to work in the cave and was richly rewarded. In the very middle of the stone bed from which the skeletons had been removed were the remains of hearths, chipped flints and other tools and weapons, and the bones of reindeer, bears, rhinos and hyenas. Many of the tools and weapons were made of reindeer antler. When had reindeer been abundant in southern France? And what manner of people had lived in the Reindeer Age?

For the next few years Mr. Lartet worked ceaselessly on the prehistoric story. As paleontologists had been working on a time scale on which could be charted the development of all life, Mr. Lartet now planned a scale of human development within the epoch of the Stone Age. He associated man in the early, tropical period with the mammoth, mastodon and rhinoceros; in the glacial period, with reindeer; and in the temperate period which followed, with aurochs (wild oxen). This was somewhat altered by later scientists, but it was a beginning of a calendar of events for human history.

After the discoveries at Aurignac, for a long time little new was added to the story of the Reindeer man. Then a railroad construction brought new revelations. Near the town of Cro-Magnon blasting had dislodged enough rock in a cliff to bring a cave into plain sight—a cave that sheltered five human skeletons.

By this time (the year was 1868) public interest had been aroused in strange skeletons, and before long Louis Lartet was asked to examine the cave. He was the son of Edouard Lartet, now too old to undertake strenuous activity.

Young Louis found a situation such as his father had seen in Aurignac. There were hearths, bones from which meat and marrow had been eaten, tools and weapons of flint and many objects made of reindeer antler. And he could examine the skeletons that lay among these remains. They were of two men, two women and a small baby. Soon the type of people they represented—the early Homo sapiens of Europe—became generally known as the Cro-Magnon people, but Reindeer men is used occasionally to describe them just as the time in which they lived is called the Reindeer Age.

Even after Cro-Magnon man had been accepted as a human ancestor, the discoverers of his remarkable art work met with disbelief. The first cave paintings to be found were in Altamira, Spain. A hunter first stumbled upon a cave there in the same year that Louis Lartet was exploring in Cro-Magnon. It was in 1873 that Don Marcellino, a Spanish nobleman who had heard of the exciting finds in France, decided to investigate in Altamira. His twelve-year-old daughter Maria begged to go with him and, armed only with candles, they stepped cautiously into the dark cave. As her father investigated near the entrance Maria wriggled and wormed her way through fallen rock and along a narrow passage. Suddenly another chamber opened before her, and here the candlelight showed a startling sight. The ceiling was covered with paintings of bison—a great herd of them, some charging, some sleeping, some standing quietly. They were done in vivid glowing tones of brown, yellow, red, violet, black and white. In excitement and fright Maria cried out for her father, and quickly Don Marcellino made his way over the rock to join her. His amazement surpassed that of his daughter. This was something scarcely to be believed even if you were looking at it! The colors were fresh as if they had just been put on. But surely the creators of this work must have known bison at first hand to portray them so perfectly; and that would set the time they had been made back to the Ice Age when bison—and Cro-Magnon man—had lived in Spain.

Don Marcellino was thrilled by this astounding evidence of prehistoric life, but when he took news of it to the world away from Altamira his story fell on deaf ears. The "experts" declared paint could not have stayed so bright for fifteen thousand years. The paintings, they said, must have been made recently with the idea of confusing historians!

However, it seemed the age of discovery was truly at hand. Before long another example of cave art was uncovered. This time it was in southern France in the village of La Mouthe. The investigations of a doctor, Emile Riviére, led to the uncovering of a narrow passageway behind what had been living quarters for Cro-Magnon man. Here walls and ceiling were covered with handsome engravings of bison, reindeer, ibex and wild horses. Again the experts scoffed, but finally were persuaded to visit the cave. There they saw the evidence with their own eyes: how the color of the engravings matched exactly the color of the rock next to them (had they been made recently they would have had a different tone), and how the passageway was filled with clay so that no one, for countless years, could have stood in it to work. As one scientist after another left the cave, he gave a new verdict. This art, and undoubtedly the paintings at Altamira, were the work of the Cro-Magnon people. Meanwhile a similarly decorated cave had been discovered not far from Bordeaux; less than five years later still another one was found. Now serious attention was given to the subject of cave paintings, and a young abbé, Henri Breuil, came to the fore as a brilliant interpreter of prehistoric art. Tirelessly he studied the caves and traced or copied the pictures. In Altamira he worked eight hours a day for three weeks, lying on his back in the candlelit recesses, so that he could reproduce the bison with accuracy. Before long (in 1905) the paintings that had been hidden away from human eyes since the Ice Age were published for all the world to see. To date, at least seventy decorated caves have been discovered.

What became of Cro-Magnon man? He knew how to use fire for warmth and cooking. He had developed tools and weapons for hunting. He had the skill and intelligence to execute works of art. Was he not equipped to survive whatever changes might come to his surroundings? Apparently not. With the last retreat of the glaciers, the animal population began to disappear from the European scene. The woolly rhinoceros, the mammoth, the great bison decreased in numbers to the vanishing point. The vitally important reindeer moved northward, staying close to the ice sheets. The Reindeer Age—or the Old Stone Age—had come to a close. It was time for Homo sapiens to move forward in a number of ways.

As the curtain goes up on the New Stone Age (sometimes called "Polished Stone Age") we find many things familiar in our present-day world. One of the most intriguing is the presence of an animal in the "family circle." It is a dog—until now just another wild creature. But man has learned that this beast can be of value in the hunt. Perhaps he found young pups without a mother and brought them to his cave and they grew tame and friendly. Or perhaps, hungry and cold, dogs hopefully looked into caves for handouts of food. However it began, by the New Stone Age a partnership was established, and man had learned the value and pleasures of keeping domesticated animals. Gradually cattle, pigs and sheep became a part of the human scene.

One change of tremendous importance we can connect directly with the term "Polished Stone Age." No longer are people taking the land as they

New Stone Age family with pet dogs

find it. They are chopping down trees, clearing land for planting seeds and to obtain material for many kinds of woodwork. The stone axes used for cutting wood have polished edges rather than being roughly chipped. This type of ax is more sturdy and has a deeper, cleaner bite. Besides the art of polishing stone, these more advanced people have discovered how to choose certain types of clay, mix it with water and treat it with heat, thus creating pottery. They also work out the principles of weaving.

As these people gathered fruit and seeds to add to their diet of meat, it is possible some fell to the earth and soon produced new plants. This did not go unnoticed and at last men began to plant seeds purposefully. It might seem that once people had begun to raise crops they would no longer be wandering huntsmen. However, their farming was very primitive indeed. Trees were cut down, the brush and wood burned, and the seeding done around the stumps. No treatment was given the soil. As a result one or two crops robbed the earth of its richness, and a new clearing had to be made. Before long the forest over a large area would be used up, and a group of hopeful farmers had no choice but to move to a new area.

Fortunately in spite of this wasteful system Europe was not quickly reduced to open meadows. Forests grew luxuriantly again after they had been passed by, and it was not until the Middle Ages, when steel had replaced polished-stone axes, that man's heritage of abundant trees began to disappear.

Meanwhile farming was by no means limited to Europe. On the continent of Africa, too, Homo sapiens had been making great strides toward civilization. From the upper stretches of the Nile River through Palestine and Syria and on through the Middle East people were growing wheat and barley and cutting the grain with straight flint sickles. They lived in mud-brick houses and raised cattle, sheep, goats and pigs. They made pottery and wove linen cloth from flax. Neanderthal people and even Cro-Magnon man were beginning to seem very, very far in the past.

Chapter XVI

PREHISTORIC AMERICANS

Thus far in our story of man's development
to the time of recorded history we have
followed events only in Europe and Asia. What was
happening on our own continent while the Cro-
Magnon people were taking over the caves of the
Neanderthal, and when the Reindeer men were
making their first attempts at farming? Were bronze-
skinned tribes already established here, or were beasts
and birds the chief American citizens?

The answers that scientists give to these questions
have changed in recent years. With all the exploring
and fossil hunting that had been done in America,
until 1926 no evidence of very early people had been
uncovered. It seemed that humans must have been
here no more than five thousand years—possibly
only three thousand. The man who first stumbled
on the trail of "Americans" still earlier than that
time was named Jesse Figgins. He was in charge of

an expedition to the fossil-rich area of Folsom, New Mexico, searching for bones of mammals that had been extinct many thousands of years. As he was digging, something astonishing caught the eye of one of his companions. Two pieces of chipped flint! Now the story of Mr. Boucher de Perthes finding chipped flint in France, just a hundred years before, was repeated: someone who understood the importance of such a relic had found it and would proceed to follow through on all its possibilities. Mr. Figgins and his friends did just that. They dug tirelessly in the dirt and clay, paying little attention, now, to bison skulls with wide-spreading horns that had been exciting discoveries a short time before. It was evidence of man they wanted.

When they found, embedded in clay that actually covered the rib of a giant bison, other pieces of flint evidently chipped by human hands, they felt they had indisputable proof of a hunt by men in the time of the Ice Age. Especially was it valuable evidence when the broken pieces could be fitted together to form the point of a dart. But even though all this evidence was shipped to a museum laboratory for examination, very few people were ready to change their minds and believe that man's ancestors had been on this continent as early as the Ice Age. So Mr. Figgins returned to Folsom and carried on his hunt for dart points among the fossil bones. When he did find more he telegraphed invitations to the leading scientific institutions to send representatives to see for themselves. The scientists accepted and there, in a remote section of New Mexico, they looked at the fossils and agreed: man had lived here ten thousand years ago and hunted giant bison, now long extinct.

But even with this acceptance, other scientists still hesitated to believe. They wanted more proof, and many of them got out and hunted for it. As a result, evidence of "Folsom man" began to be found in many parts of the high plains on the eastern slopes of the Rockies. And at Yuma, Colorado, quantities of long, slender flint points were uncovered. These apparently had been made by a similar type of people not very long after those found at Folsom were in use.

Here and there chance discoveries revealed other glimpses of American people during the latter part of the Ice Age. Near Mexico City two different skeletons of Indians were found in the same layer of earth with mammoth remains. In each case the Indian had apparently been hunting mammoth when he became mired in the swampy edge of a lake which then filled much of the Valley of Mexico. He died where he was trapped, and his bones and weapons, together with the fossilized bones of the mammoths which also were trapped, remained to tell the story. In Minnesota, death by drowning apparently resulted in the skeleton of a young woman being preserved through many thousands of years. And in other places throughout the continent tools of stone and bone were discovered in connection with long-extinct

Bison Hunt

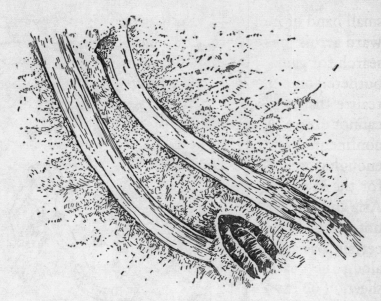

Spear tip as found with bison's ribs

animals or in other circumstances that pointed to their belonging to the glacial age.

It was disappointing that more actual prehistoric skeletons were not found, but there seemed to be a good explanation of their scarcity. These early Americans were hunters and wanderers; they did not stay long in one place. They did not live in caves and probably did not bury their dead. It was by very rare chance that conditions were favorable for the preservation of their skeletons as fossils.

But scarce though skeletons might be, enough evidence was gathered to put together pieces of the jigsaw puzzle and produce a picture of the first human immigrants to the New World. The picture shows a small band of hunters—a family group—moving east-ward across the far corner of Siberia. In their endless search for game they come to a narrow strip of land, bordered on either side by an icy sea. They may not realize that it is only a narrow strip; certainly they cannot dream that it is the passageway to a great new continent. But they press on, hoping only to find enough game to keep them alive. The cold is intense, for the last of the great glaciers still covers much of Asia and North America. The group of hunters have not much choice as to which way to go because only certain passages across the Bering Strait region and along the coast of Alaska are left open by the ice sheet. The wanderers follow the open trails—and come at last to the warm inviting fields and forests of the more southern part of the continent.

There was not one such adventurous party but many. For thousands of years similar groups made more or less the same journey, using the land bridge from Siberia to Alaska on which a number of mam-mals were migrating. Then the historic passageway came to an end. The waters rose and Bering Strait could no longer be crossed by foot travelers. How-ever, by this time the Americas had a human popu-lation of their own. The questing hunters had doubt-less wandered from the Arctic shore of Alaska south-ward between the ice-covered mountains of the west and the glacier that still covered eastern Canada. On they went, some stopping and adapting themselves to warm and even tropical climates, others continuing through the many variations in climate and hunting conditions until they arrived at the southern tip of South America. Gradually small groups occupied scattered areas throughout the entire hemisphere; and gradually they went through the same general development toward "culture" that was taking place in the Old World. It is not surprising that, with the vastly different conditions under which various groups lived, their activities and customs should vary also. So, in time, a number of different cultures were established, the three large divisions in North America being the Woodlands, the Arctic and the Pacific.

On the west coast, so great were the riches of the earth that the people who stopped there had good reason to "settle." Acorns and nuts were plentiful, and their meat was a nourishing food. Salmon could be caught at will; rabbits and deer could be killed with throwing sticks. There was no need to migrate after game nor was there even need for planting. Among the earliest "Californians," therefore, small villages began to form, and basket weaving became at once the chief art work and practical production of the people. The baskets were woven so closely that they could be used, instead of pottery jars, for holding water. Often they were handsomely decorated with feathers and beading worked in with the yucca fiber. To their simple garments of animal skins the women added basketry skullcaps and sometimes sandals made of yucca cord. Occasionally when a person died his family would bury him with a large basket placed over his head. Shallow caves gave all the shelter these people needed; the climate brought no hardships.

As the Basket Makers developed the more closely knit feeling of a tribe and began to dance and act out myths that had captured their imagination, they learned to make earth lodges—partly underground—in which tribal ceremonies could be performed. Ancient lodges of this type have been discovered all the way to Siberia. In time the Basket Makers also began

Basket makers, Mesa Verde

to create clay pots. They fashioned needles out of turkey bones and used bow and arrow for hunting.

To the north of the Basket Makers, nature was generous also. The special wealth of the region was magnificent timber, and it was about woodwork that the people of the northwest coast built up their own special kind of culture.

Today in the Far North, from the south coast of Alaska around the American Arctic to Greenland and Labrador, we know the hardy Eskimo hunters. Considering their bleak surroundings, their culture advanced to a remarkable degree. Their igloos (in some area made of snow blocks but more generally earth-covered houses of stone or whalebone) and summer tents, their harpoons and kayaks, all show inventive minds and clever hands. It is believed that Eskimos are not nearly so old in America as the Indians' ancestors. At least until now, two thousand years is as far back as their life has been traced.

In the eastern woodlands of North America the story of man goes back much further than that. To this vast region had come some of the nomads from Asia, and even as men were doing in the Old World they developed polished stone tools. Stone knives, scrapers, axes and spears were expertly used by the huntsmen. Hooks, needles and awls of bone helped with domestic work. Tailored clothes fashioned of worked skin were a great improvement on earlier garments of animal hide. They not only ate meat but varied their diet with wild vegetables and great

Mound Builders

quantities of sea food. Something like four thousand years ago such Indians built an expert system of weirs for trapping fish in the tidewater of the Charles River, in Massachusetts. Some of its remains still exist deep in the silt under a section of Boston!

In time these people added pottery making to their accomplishments. Still later they became familiar with agriculture, and grew squash, corn and gourds. And something else was added to their culture which was concerned not with making a good living but with their treatment of the dead. This was mound building.

Since the settlement of North America by white people, the work of the Mound Builders had puzzled scientists and ordinary citizens alike. Man-made hills, some covering several acres and some fairly small, were discovered from time to time, strewn from the Mississippi River to the Appalachian Mountains and from Wisconsin to the Gulf of Mexico. In shape they varied from cones to the forms of all kinds of animals and human beings. Altogether there were many thousands of them.

Pioneers pushing westward often questioned Indians about these strange hills. Had *they* built them? The answer was "No." Futhermore the Indians had no idea of how the mysterious mounds got where they were.

At last real investigation was begun. Carefully men dug into the soil, and as they dug they uncovered bit by bit the picture of a civilization far older than that of the American Indians who met the first European colonists. Here, in company with human skeletons, were copper breastplates and all manner of artistic objects made of silver, mica, obsidian and river pearls. There were stone statuettes, too, portraying animals as well as human heads. There was even cloth made of fiber from bark, nettles and grasses. The mounds had surely been constructed by expert artists and craftsmen. The Woodlands Indians of a later day were simple deer and buffalo hunters; they knew nothing of the use of metals.

The mounds themselves received careful attention from investigators. While many were small and simple, others were enormous, containing floors which apparently had been the scene of certain ceremonial rites. Some of the large mounds had flat tops that evidently had served as bases for temples or forts of some kind. In Ohio was the Great Serpent Mound, consisting of earth molded in the form of a super-giant snake. For more than a thousand feet the great "coils" wound along the edge of a high cliff, ending in a huge head situated on a rocky precipice. The jaws were open and held an oval figure in the middle of which was burnt stone. Had this been an altar? Did the Mound Builders worship this "serpent"? In this mound there was no sign of burials.

Scientists studied the evidence for a long time before reaching conclusions as to where the Mound Builders had come from and what their fate had been. It became clear that the simple and fairly small burial mounds were constructed by Indians in the eastern woodlands well over a thousand years ago. Later, Indians from Mexico and Central America migrated northward and eastward until they came to "mound builders'" territory. Here they settled and in time their customs and artistic talents greatly influenced the type of mounds that were constructed. The structures of earth became larger and more complex, and into the elaborate "graves" went silver ornaments, stone carvings and other works of art. Many of the carved human figures placed within them were costumed in a style strongly suggesting the garb of Mexican priests, and in their ears were copper ornaments carved in Mexican fashion. The Great Serpent Mound was another strong reminder of Mexico: the ancient people of that region had worshipped a feathered serpent.

After thriving for hundreds of years the Mound Builders disappeared quite suddenly from the American scene. Apparently disease was the enemy that conquered them. By the year 1500 a few Spanish colonists had moved into the eastern regions and soon epidemics were plaguing them. The diseases spread to the nearby natives, and before long the Mound Builders were a people belonging definitely to "the past."

The glimpse of a culture from "south of the border" which is revealed in the great mounds is a perfect introduction to prehistoric man in South America. Although less is known about the early events on that continent than on our own, discoveries of very ancient relics have been made. Down at the bleak, southernmost tip there are caves that show evidence of having had human occupants over a period of nine thousand years. These people were hunters. In other southern parts of South America and in Central Brazil there were primitive hunters also. But at the same time certain tribes were exploring the advantages of planting. Indeed when we look at the foods that were first produced in South America, it is easy to think of this land as the "garden spot" of the prehistoric world. Corn, potatoes, sweet potatoes, beans, tomatoes, squash, chocolate, vanilla and peanuts (as well as many other plants of less importance), all were developed there from wild plants. Possibly some of them, such as corn, tomatoes and squash, were domesticated in more than one South American region, and a few were discovered in Central America as well. The art of pottery making was begun at a far-distant time and developed slowly in these areas. But then important strides were made. Discoveries show that three thousand years ago expert and handsome work was done with clay, cloth was woven on looms, and artistic creations were made in metal.

Altogether a well-advanced culture was on its way among groups of people living from the central Andes on up into Mexico. And it seems likely that this culture was the root from which grew the later remarkable civilizations that we know as Maya, Inca and Aztec.

Thus scientists followed a long journey—from the earliest cave dwellers in Asia and Europe to the beginnings of recorded history in both the New and Old Worlds. These experts are known as archaeologists, a word that originally meant "the track of man or beast." But today the archaeologist specializes in man, leaving the remains of other kinds of life to his fellow scientist, the paleontologist.

Chapter XVII

ADVENTURES IN PREHISTORIC EXPLORING

In following the story of prehistoric life we have given more attention to the people who made discoveries of early man than to those who discovered fossils of beasts, birds and plants. This is only because the far greater numbers of such finds make it impossible to give the same kind of detail. However, any account of this vast subject would not seem complete without including some outstanding personalities in the field of paleontology and a few of their dramatic explorations.

Baron Georges Cuvier was a great pioneer. He explained clearly, for the first time, the relationships among various animals with backbones, and his studies were based on fossil as well as living animals. He is considered the founder of the science of vertebrate paleontology. While Baron Cuvier worked in his native France early in the nineteenth century, Sir Richard Owen carried on studies of long-vanished

196

animals in England. His christening a certain type of reptile "Dinosauria" gave rise to the widely popular name of "dinosaur."

In our own country, a pioneer work in vertebrate paleontology was begun in the early part of the nineteenth century by Joseph Leidy, a professor at the University of Pennsylvania. However, it was not until after the Civil War that any important fossil-hunting program was developed. Then it was that two brilliant men, Edward D. Cope and O. C. Marsh, began a well-planned campaign of fossil hunting, literally following in the footsteps of geologists who who were then studying the great expanses of the west. It was a time when hostile Indians were among the dangers that explorers had to meet, but nothing stopped them in the mission to which they had dedicated their lives.

By the time Cope and Marsh passed away, Henry Fairfield Osborn, a professor from Princeton University, had established a department of vertebrate paleontology at the American Museum of Natural History in New York. To the staff of this department came a group of enthusiastic, gifted scientists whose collecting work in the field and studies in the museum's laboratories soon opened many new pages in the prehistoric story. Other museums followed with important contributions and today, though much is already known about the past, scientists are unceasingly applying their skills and knowledge to discovering still more.

197

Because the adventures of museum people often make exciting reading, the patience and hard work involved are sometimes forgotten. We might look at an exhibit of the skeleton of a giant tortoise that lived a million years ago, and learn that it was found in the hills of northern India by Dr. Barnum Brown. What fun to go to India and come upon the skeleton of this great monster which, in the flesh, must have weighed a ton! But when Dr. Brown discovered the skeleton it was broken into thousands of scattered pieces, many of them no larger than a man's hand. So great would be the task of assembling them that he continued to explore for a year and a half, hoping for a more perfect shell.

At last Dr. Brown decided he must bring his original find back to the museum. The trip was begun by transporting more than eight hundred pounds of bones by camel away from the Himalaya Mountains; ship and truck completed the journey. All that remained, then, was to study the bones and organize them into a skeleton. Under Dr. Brown's direction one paleontologist worked on this job for well over a year, with frequent help from the entire laboratory force.

This great tortoise is by no means Dr. Brown's best-known find. It was he who introduced mighty Tyrannosaurus to our modern world! Some fifty years ago, when exploring in the rugged hills of South Dakota, Dr. Brown came upon part of an extraordinary skeleton. Two years later careful

The Bad Lands, rich hunting grounds for fossils

searching unearthed more bones of the same kind of animal, but no complete form. Then he heard that the Bad Lands of Montana, nearly a hundred and fifty miles away, might prove good hunting grounds. It took a five-day cross-country march to reach the wilderness of cliffs, gullies and ravines that make up the Bad Lands. He made camp at Hell Creek—and once again the search was on. This time it was successful. There lay an almost perfect skeleton of Tyrannosaurus! Most of the bones were in the very position in which they fell when the great dinosaur died.

Bringing Tyrannosaurus back to the museum meant two summers of backbreaking work by a group of men. Plows, scrapers and dynamite were used to slice off the hillside in which the bones were buried, then the sandstone blocks containing the bones had to be dragged to a distant railroad station. A few years later, still working in the Bad Lands, Dr. Brown found another Tyrannosaurus skeleton. The fossil remains of these great flesh-eating reptiles are now prized exhibits at the American Museum. Besides Tyrannosaurus, Dr. Brown has collected many other dinosaur skeletons, including the enormous duckbill variety.

It was only a few years ago that another historic discovery was made in a remote section of the desert

Dr. Barnum Brown examining fossil in Bad Lands

of New Mexico. Dr. Edwin Colbert had gone exploring for the American Museum to learn more about rocks of the Triassic period—the opening phase of the dinosaur age. By the time of this expedition modern aids were making certain phases of field work less difficult than in pioneering days. Dr. Colbert and his companions could ride in a jeep from their headquarters to the brilliantly colored cliffs where they thought fossil treasure might be buried. But, once there, they had to depend on footwork; and for hour after hour in the hot glaring sunlight they clambered about the foot of the cliffs and up and down the slopes. One day had been especially unrewarding but when Dr. Colbert returned to the jeep a fellow explorer, George Whitaker, who had been hunting in another direction, had a handful of bone fragments to show. At first glance they did not look very impressive. None was larger than a walnut; and some were from an animal's backbone and others were bits of limb bones. However, one little piece caused Dr. Colbert to feel the tremendous thrill that comes to any treasure hunter at the first glimpse of his prize. It was a piece of claw; and because of its size and shape he realized at once that it had belonged to one of the earliest and smallest of all dinosaurs. For years he had been hoping to find well-preserved remains of this ancient reptile! Since the pioneer days of paleontologist Cope it had been known only by occasional fragments.

Little time was lost in beginning work at the spot where Mr. Whitaker had picked up the loose pieces of bone. It was on a long sloping cliff where loose rocks slid out from underfoot with almost every step. The site did not look very promising, but as the explorers brushed away the crumbling dirt, fossils began to appear in surprising numbers. It was especially amazing to see that almost all the bones were of the "pocket-size" dinosaur. Small as the dinosaur was, this was big-scale discovery! Dr. Colbert hastened to make plans for serious digging. With the aid of a bulldozer a road was built across the desert to ease the job of bringing supplies; another fossil expert flew down from New York—and work went into high gear.

Claw of one of the earliest dinosaurs, found in New Mexico

Since the process of removing bones from rock could be done properly only in the museum laboratory, the big task was to cut the sandstone tomb of the dinosaurs into blocks small enough to be moved, and because the precious bones lay in an almost solid mass, this was a real problem. It was done at last by making the cuts curve around bones instead of going in a straight line, or by removing a bone after carefully showing its position on a diagram so that its connection with neighboring fossils would be remembered exactly. Once the blocks were cut and encased in plaster of paris, the bulldozer made quick work of dragging them to a point from which they could be shipped eastward.

It was in this fashion that the early dinosaur Coelophysis became headline news for modern scientists, and Dr. Colbert could ready for exhibition an accurate picture of a reptile almost two hundred million years old.

When Dr. Roy Chapman Andrews led fossil-hunting expeditions into central Asia, he did not have hostile Indians to watch for, but groups of armed bandits roaming the countryside made rifles necessary equipment for the scientists. The great Gobi Desert in the heart of Mongolia seemed to be a likely storehouse of fossils, but until 1922 very little exploring had been done there. Not only bandits but vast stretches of gravel (far too coarse to be called sand), unbearable heat in summer and bitter cold in winter made it a forbidden land. The few hardy souls who had tried to work there came away defeated.

Dr. Andrews made the bold plan of using motor-cars for transportation; this was twenty years before the jeep, and not many people believed the desert could be crossed in this fashion. But, undiscouraged, the Central Asiatic Expedition assembled at the edge of the great Mongolian plateau. There were forty men, Mongolian and Chinese workers as well as the American scientists, eight cars and a hundred and fifty camels. These beasts of burden were to follow along with gasoline and other supplies.

After three days of travel over deep ruts, mud-holes and boundless grassy plains, Dr. Andrews called a halt. There stood a gravel bluff that looked like good fossil-hunting ground. Camp was set up nearby while the paleontologists busied themselves checking on their prospects for discoveries. Within a matter of minutes they had their answer: they had already picked up handfuls of fossil bones—the first ever to be found on the Mongolian plateau. The area proved an enormous graveyard of dinosaur bones. So exciting was each day's hunt that everyone at camp, even to the Chinese cooks and Mongolian workers, wanted to "get into the act." No matter what official duties anyone had, most of his time was spent on the limestone ridge looking for bones.

Not only dinosaur bones but fossil remains of plants, mammals and other fossil animals were found almost every day. One of the most important discoveries was the ancestor of Triceratops, the great three-horned dinosaur of North America. But still more excitement was to come the next season when dinosaur *eggs* came to light.

It was in a region the explorers had seen on their way out of the Gobi the year before and which they had named the Flaming Cliffs because of the beautiful red and pink color of the sandstone. To the Flaming Cliffs Dr. Andrews led his caravan. They encamped in the middle of the afternoon—and before dark every fossil hunter in the party had chalked up a skeleton for himself! The next day George Olsen, a member of the party, made the startling announcement that he had just seen some large fossil eggs. No one was ready to believe that they could be eggs of "the" reptile but all hurried to have a look. Dr. Walter Granger, one of the truly great collectors of fossils, carefully examined the three egg-shaped objects which evidently had broken out of a shelf of sandstone and were lying on the ground. The outer covering looked like a regular brown eggshell, except that it was thicker and completely petrified. Where the stone shell was broken, the inside was shown to be solid red sandstone.

"No doubt about it," was Dr. Granger's opinion. "These eggs were laid by a dinosaur!"

Other eggs were glimpsed still embedded in rock. They were not disturbed, but a large block of sandstone containing them was shipped to the museum. When this was finally worked over, the sandstone being chipped away with greatest care, thirteen more eggs were disclosed. In two of them were the skeletons of unhatched dinosaur babies!

Two years later Dr. Andrews again led the Central Asiatic Expeditions into action. Again they went to the Flaming Cliffs. The months of weathering since their former trip had made great changes in the cliffs and on the ground. Old surfaces had cracked and been blown away; the soft sandstone had countless new treasures to reveal. Many, many eggs were found. It seemed that during the Age of Reptiles this particular region must have been as dry as in modern times, and was just the kind of spot that dinosaurs favored for their nests. Only sometimes conditions had not been right for eggs to hatch; but they were exactly right for the purposes of fossil hunters who were to come along millions of years later.

One of the most tremendous of all fossil treasures required no expedition to dangerous, distant parts of the earth. It lay just outside the city of Los Angeles—waiting to be discovered. Rancho La Brea, as it is called, was actually discovered twice as a paleontologist's prize before it was given full recognition. *Brea* is the Spanish word for "pitch" or "tar," and the ranch name, given back in the days when

Rancho La Brea tar pool

California was a part of Mexico, was well chosen. On the grounds for an area from a quarter of a mile to a full mile across, black tar oozed up through little holes in the ground and spread out into pools. As it mixed with sand and dust it hardened into asphalt so that the edges around a pool were firm, but beyond a few steps it was soft and gummy. When a film of dust blew over it, it looked like solid earth; when rain water lay on it, it looked like an ordinary puddle. As a result, the pools proved to be a giant animal trap. Creatures that came to drink, or to prey upon others they saw drinking, were sucked down by the sticky tar from which there was no rescue.

Less than a hundred years ago the owner of Rancho La Brea was doing a flourishing business marketing the asphalt tar. Preparing it for sale would have been simple had it not been for the animal bones which workmen were constantly having to dig out of the asphalt. Heaps of them began to accumulate all about the pools. Though they were a nuisance, the owner was rather curious about them, especially when a particularly strange skull or tooth turned up. One so aroused his interest that he showed it to a visiting naturalist. The naturalist was thunderstruck. He identified it as having belonged to a great saber-toothed tiger that lived early in the Ice Age!

Strangely enough, in spite of this discovery nothing was done about investigating the tar pools for another thirty years. They then came to the attention of John Merriam, a professor at the University of California. Professor Merriam lost no time hurrying to Rancho La Brea, and this was the real beginning of its discovery. There were found in the asphalt fossil bones not only of saber-toothed tigers (the skulls of two thousand of them) but of horses, camels, giant sloths, mammoths, mastodons, vultures, wolves and many other beasts and birds. It was fantastic yet understandable, as even today other sticky tar pools located nearby are a menace and have to be guarded to keep domestic animals from becoming trapped.

There must have been many a dreadful scene at Rancho La Brea through the ages. Professor Merriam could picture a peaceful creature coming to drink there. Unsuspectingly it steps on the gummy tar. As it struggles to get free it attracts the attention of a saber-toothed tiger, which quickly pounces for a kill. Now two animals are trapped, and as they flounder and slowly sink a vulture flies down to tear at their flesh. But soon its wings dip low and the feathers are coated with tar and the pool has claimed another victim. Over and over this drama is repeated with varying casts of characters, and as time goes by their skeletons become a jumbled mass of fossil bones. It is a prehistoric gold mine, this "gold" being relics of the past. Nowhere else in the world have the remains of so many extinct animals been found in one place.

Fossil by fossil, discovery after discovery, the jigsaw puzzle of our earth's past is being put together. Still there are many missing pieces; still there are parts that do not fit exactly into place. That is the challenge to paleontologists and archaeologists who are working constantly to solve mysteries which must have an explanation if the proper key can be found. And it is exciting to realize that any alert person may find one of the "keys." A dry river bed may show impressions of sea creatures millions of years old. In rocky areas where melting glaciers deposited materials pushed from farther north, there may be a great variety of fossil-bearing fragments. Quarries and construction excavations provide amateur fossil hunters with made-to-order collecting grounds. The excitement of tracking down prehistoric life—from trilobite to saber-toothed tiger —is possible for all to share.

INDEX

211